Physics Workshop 1

UNDERSTANDING ENERGY and FORCES

SEYMOUR ROSEN

Globe Book Company, Inc.
Englewood Cliffs, New Jersey

GLOBE BOOK
COMPANY

THE AUTHOR

Seymour Rosen received his B.A. and M.S. degrees from Brooklyn College. Mr. Rosen taught science at the Edward B. Shallow Intermediate School in Brooklyn, New York for twenty-three years. He currently teaches at the Springfield Gardens Intermediate School in Queens, New York.

Mr. Rosen was a contributing participant in a teacher-training program for the development of science curriculum for the New York City Board of Education.

Cover Design: Berg Design
Cover Photograph: D. Newman, Visuals Unlimited

Text Photographs

DuPont Company: 34
Helena Frost: 64, 156
Frederic Lewis: 164
Swiss National Tourist Office: 172
UPI: 148

ISBN: 1-55675-709-3

PRINTED IN THE UNITED STATES OF AMERICA   5 6 7 8 9 0

CONTENTS

1 What is energy? 1

2 What is potential energy?
What is kinetic energy? 9

3 How does energy change? 15

4 What happens to energy that is not used? 23

5 What is a force? 29

6 What is the force of gravity? 35

7 What happens when forces work at the same time? 41

8 What is work? 51

9 How can you move something with less force? 57

10 How can a small force move a heavy object? 65

11 What is mechanical advantage? 71

12 What price do you pay to gain mechanical advantage? 77

13 How does an inclined plane make work easier? 83

14 How do you figure the M.A. of an inclined plane? 89

15 How is a wedge like an inclined plane? 95

16 How is a screw like an inclined plane?   101

17 How does a pulley make work easier?   107

18 How does a wheel and axle make work easier?   113

19 What do you call the parts of a lever?   119

20 How can you find the mechanical advantage of a lever?   125

21 When does a lever balance?   131

22 How do objects balance?   137

23 Why do objects tilt over?   143

24 How can objects of the same size have different weights?   149

25 Why does a ship float?   157

26 What is pressure?   165

27 What happens to the weight of an object when it is under water?   173

28 What happens to the weight of a floating object?   179

Keeping Up With Science

Flying By Pedal Power   34
Baseball Curves   50
Blimps on the Rise   164

BEFORE YOU BEGIN . . . .

Did you ever ride downhill on a skateboard? You have to *balance* yourself. The *wheels* roll so you don't have to use much *energy* to get yourself going. And, the *force* of *gravity* pulls you down the hill.

This book is about all of these things—energy, force, gravity, and simple machines, like the wheel and axle. You will learn about why you can balance on a see-saw. You will even learn a few secrets about how to lose weight scientifically: by going underwater or into outer space.

This book is set up in a special way. Each Aim begins with the things you'll need to know. This is followed by a series of exercises. Take your time on these. And look back to the beginning of the Aim when you're not sure of an answer. There will be experiments along the way—and a few surprises, too.

So get your skateboard ready and let's get rolling!

SCIENCE SAFETY

Science is the study of the world around you. The study of any branch of science includes "learning by doing." Investigations, experiments, demonstrations. Activities in which you are involved. *You* make things happen.

Safety is a very important part of these activities. Even if you are only *reading* about an investigation, you should know about the safety precautions that MUST be taken. The following SAFETY ALERT SYMBOLS are designed to call these precautions to your attention. They appear on pages wherever any of these dangers are present.

Safety Goggles   **Lab Apron or Coat**   Safety goggles and a laboratory apron or coat should be worn for all activities or investigations.

Open Flame   When working near an open flame, be sure that hair and loose clothing are secured in some manner.

Poison   Many chemicals are poisonous, or toxic. *Never* taste, touch, or smell any unknown substance unless told to do so by your teacher.

Caustic Substances   *Caustic* (KAW stik) substances can burn your skin, eyes, and clothing. Handle these substances with extreme care. Acids and bases (such as lye) are caustic.

Toxic Vapors   *Never* inhale any vapors directly. To test the odor of a substance, use your hand to waft the vapors to your nose.

Sharp Objects   *Always* handle sharp objects with great care.

Broken Glass   Glassware, such as beakers, test tubes, glass tubing, and thermometers should be handled very carefully to avoid breakage. *Never* pick up broken glass with your bare hands.

Electric Shock   *Never* use electrical appliances near water or other liquids. Always inspect wiring for worn or broken insulation. Unplug all electric cords when not in use.

Hot Objects   When handling hot objects, use tongs or padded gloves. *Never* set hot objects directly on a desk or table top. Set them on a heat-resistant pad.

WHAT IS ENERGY?

energy: the ability to make things move

matter: anything that has weight and takes up space

AIM 1 | What is energy?

Look around. How many things do you see moving?

What makes something move? Why does a rowboat drift downstream? Why do fallen leaves fly around? What lifts a rocket off the ground? Why can you turn the page of this book?

Objects move because of *energy*. We say, then, that *energy is the ability to make things move.*

Energy is not like matter. Matter has weight and takes up space. Energy has *no weight* and *does not take up space. Energy moves matter.*

There are seven main forms of energy. They are: *heat, light, sound, chemical, atomic, electrical,* and *mechanical* [muh KAN i kul].

Heat energy, for example, moves trucks, cars, ships, and airplanes.

Sound energy vibrates the air molecules. The vibrating molecules move tiny bones in your ear. The message of sound then moves to your brain.

The energy you know best is *mechanical energy.* Mechanical energy is the energy of anything that is *already* moving.

Matter that is moving can make something else move. For example, a moving hand has mechanical energy. How many things can you move with your hands?

Wind and moving water have mechanical energy too. Did you ever see the wind or moving water move something? Sure you have! What caused that cinder to fly into your eye?

Even a thrown rock has mechanical energy. It moves something when it lands—even if it is only a bit of dirt or dust. A moving rock even moves things *before* it lands. Can you figure out what it moves?

Mechanical energy is the moving force of all machines. And everyone knows how important machines are.

ENERGY CAN MAKE THINGS MOVE

These are examples of *mechanical energy*.

Figure A

Figure B

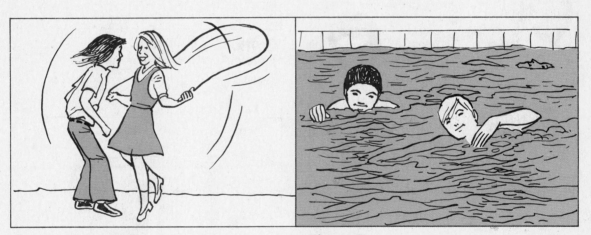

Figure C

Figure D

Figure E

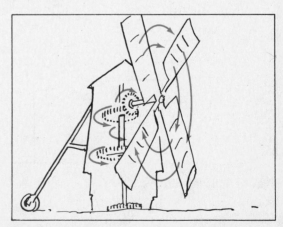

Figure F

ENERGY CAN BE IN MANY FORMS

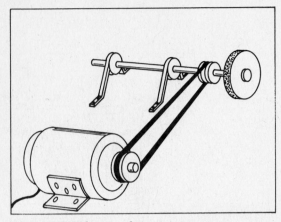

Figure G *Electrical Energy*

Figure J *Light Energy*
A radiometer turns when light hits it.

Figure H *Sound Energy*

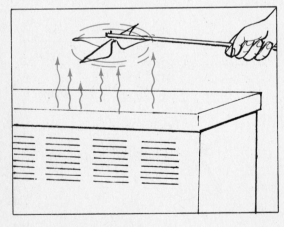

Figure I *Heat Energy*

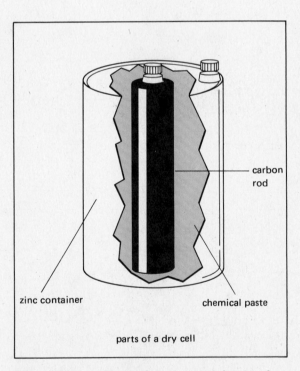

carbon
rod

zinc container

chemical paste

parts of a dry cell

Figure K *A dry cell gives us electrical energy—but it comes from chemicals.*

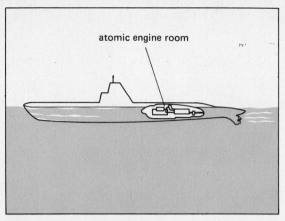

Figure L *Atomic Energy*

The energy of the atom gives off a great deal of heat. We use this heat to make things move. The energy of an atom is called atomic, or nuclear [new KLEE ar], energy.

Figure M *Living things need energy to stay alive.*

Where does this energy come from? _____

_____

_____

Complete the sentences with the choices below. Two of these
may be used twice.

---

heat	chemical	moving water
mechanical	energy	electrical
atomic	sound	space
wind	weight	light
move		

1. The ability to make things move is called _____.

2. The main forms of energy are _____, _____, _____,

   _____, _____, _____, and _____.

3. The energy of moving things is called _____ energy.

4. Moving things can make other things _____.

5. Examples of mechanical energy are _____ and _____.

6. Matter has _____ and takes up _____.

7. _____ has no weight and does not take up space.

TRUE OR
FALSE Write T on the line next to the number if the sentence is true.
Write F if the sentence is false.

---

1. _____ Energy makes things move.

2. _____ Only moving things have energy.

3. _____ There is only one kind of energy.

4. _____ Everything has the same amount of energy.

5. _____ Living things need energy.

6. _____ Air molecules can vibrate.

7. _____ Moving water is an example of electrical energy.

8. _____ Moving water can make electrical energy.

9. _____ Energy takes up space and can be weighed.

10. _____ Matter and energy are the same.

In each of the following sets of terms, one of the terms does not belong. Circle that term.

1. has weight   energy   takes up space

2. light   heat   matter

3. moving water   sound energy   moving wind

CHOOSE ONE Choose the correct word or term for each statement. Write your choice in the space.

1. _____ has weight and takes up space.
   Matter, Energy

2. _____ makes things move.
   Matter, Energy

3. Wind moving a windmill is an example of _____ energy.
   atomic, mechanical

4. _____ energy gives off a great deal of heat.
   Atomic, Sound

WORD SCRAMBLE Unscramble each of the following to form a word or term that you have read in this Aim.

1. GREYEN   _____

2. ONUDS   _____

3. TAMRET   _____

4. HITLG   _____

5. LAMCHINECA   _____

REACHING OUT

A *fuel* gives us heat energy. *Natural gas* is one kind of fuel.

1. Name two other common fuels. _____ _____

2. Why is the sun called the source of most of our energy? _____

_____

_____

_____

3. Name an energy source that does *not* come from the sun. _____

WHAT IS POTENTIAL ENERGY?
WHAT IS KINETIC ENERGY?

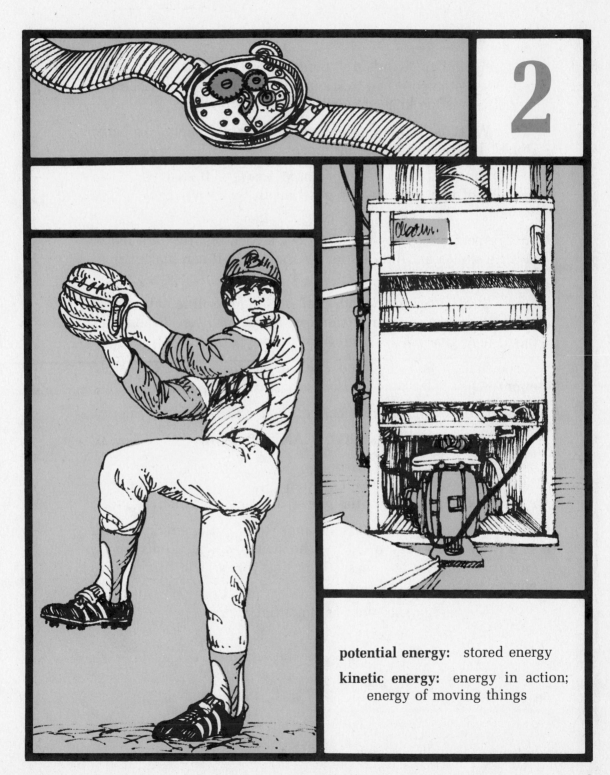

potential energy: stored energy

kinetic energy: energy in action;
energy of moving things

AIM 2 | What is potential energy?
| What is kinetic energy?

A pitcher "winds up" before throwing a ball. You wind up your watch so it can tick away the seconds. The basketball player bends his knees before he jumps.

What is happening? In each example, energy is being *stored*. It is waiting to be let loose.

Any matter can have stored energy. It can be stored because of two reasons—its *position* or its *chemistry*.

A baseball pitcher and the watch spring have stored energy because of position. So does a rock resting on a ledge. A little shove, and it falls. As the rock falls, it can make things move.

Substances like wood, coal, oil, and gasoline have stored energy because of their chemistry. They can *burn*. When they burn, they give off heat and light energy.

Scientists call stored energy *potential* [puh TEN shul] energy.

Energy in action is called *kinetic* [kuh NET ik] energy.

POTENTIAL ENERGY CAN CHANGE TO KINETIC ENERGY.

For example, a wound-up spring has *potential* energy. As it unwinds, the potential energy changes to *kinetic* energy.

Potential energy can change to kinetic energy either s l o w l y—or—very quickly. The watch spring gives up its energy s l o w l y as the seconds tick away. The pitcher lets energy loose quickly.

All energy starts out as potential energy.

POTENTIAL OR KINETIC?

Look at the paired figures A–F. Write *potential* or *kinetic* on the correct lines.

Figure A

1. _____

Figure B

2. _____

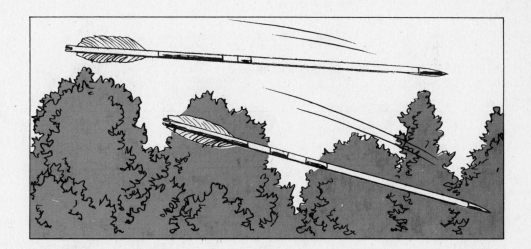

Figure C

3. _____

Figure D

4. _____

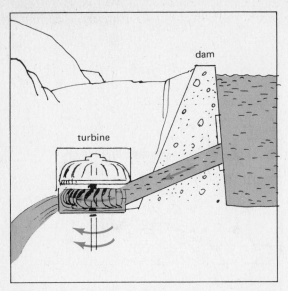

Figure E

5. _____

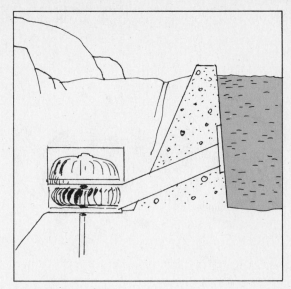

Figure F

6. _____

ATOMIC ENERGY

Figure G

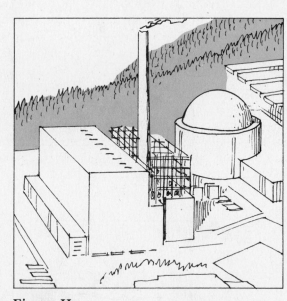

Figure H

Matter like uranium has an *enormous* amount of potential energy. Uranium is used in atomic bombs. Uranium is also used to produce electricity.

In an atomic bomb, the energy of uranium is given off *very* quickly.

In an atomic power station, its energy is given off slowly.

12

FIGURE IT OUT

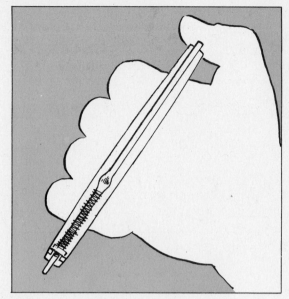

Figure I

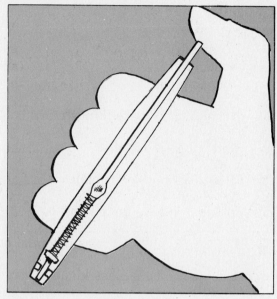

Figure J

Do you have a ball-point pen that snaps in and out? If you do, then try this.

1. Press the plunger down. The spring in the pen now has _____ energy.
   potential, kinetic

2. Now release the spring. When you released the spring, it had _____
   potential, kinetic
   energy.

3. The potential energy of the spring became kinetic energy _____.
   slowly, quickly

MATCHING   Match the two lists. Write the correct letter on the line next to each number.

1. _____ potential energy

2. _____ kinetic energy

3. _____ watch spring

4. _____ change from potential to kinetic

5. _____ oil

a) energy in action

b) has potential energy because of position

c) stored energy

d) has potential energy because of chemistry

e) can be slow or quick

Complete the sentences with the choices below. Three of these may be used twice.

chemistry	piece of coal	kinetic
potential	energy	quickly
burning coal	position	

1. The ability to make things move is called _____.

2. Stored energy is called _____ energy.

3. Energy doing a job is called _____ energy.

4. Potential energy can change to _____ energy.

5. A _____ has potential energy.

6. _____ has kinetic energy.

7. Matter has potential energy because of its _____ or its _____.

8. A pen with its plunger "in" has potential energy because of its _____.

9. Fuel oil has potential energy because of its _____.

10. Potential energy can change to kinetic energy _____ or slowly.

REACHING OUT

Rocks A and B weigh the same.

1. Which one has more potential energy? _____

2. Why? _____

3. What do you think is causing this energy of position? _____

_____

_____

Figure K

HOW DOES ENERGY CHANGE?

3

energy conversion: the change of energy from one form to another

AIM 3 | How does energy change?

Do you know how to whistle? If you blow air past your lips in a certain way, a whistling sound comes out. The moving air is not sound energy. It is mechanical energy. What happens is this. Part of the mechanical energy *changes* to sound energy.

Whistling shows us something very important. It shows us that energy can change from one form to another. We call energy changes *conversions* [kon VURZH unz]. Conversion means a change into something else.

Energy conversions are very important. You cannot live without them.

The food you eat has chemical energy. Your body converts (changes) this chemical energy to the heat energy and the mechanical energy you need to stay alive.

Your body also converts chemical energy to electrical energy. Nerves need electrical energy to carry messages. Without electrical energy, your brain would not work, your heart would not pump, and your lungs would not breathe in and out.

Energy conversions are happening around you all the time. You flip up the switch in your home and the lights go on. Electrical energy has changed to light energy. Your toaster converts electrical energy to heat energy. A fan changes electrical energy to mechanical energy. Its motor gets hot. You can also hear it. This means that some of the energy has changed to heat and sound energy.

ONE FORM OF ENERGY BECOMES ANOTHER FORM OF ENERGY

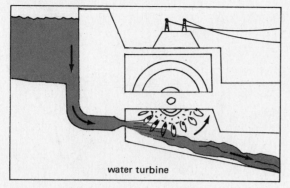

Figure A

Mechanical energy converts to electrical energy.

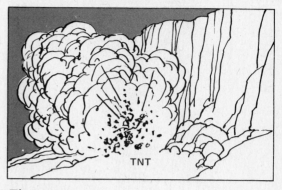

Figure B

Chemical energy converts to mechanical energy.

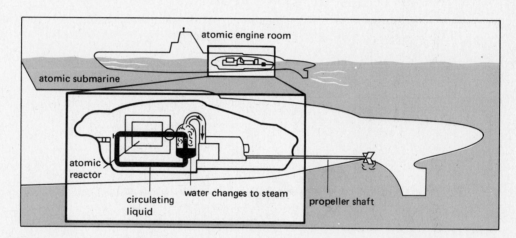

Figure C

Atomic energy converts to heat energy and then to mechanical energy.

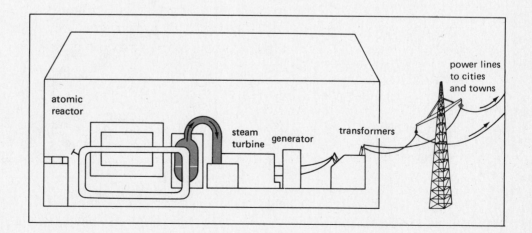

Figure D

Atomic energy converts to heat energy, then to mechanical energy, and then to electrical energy.

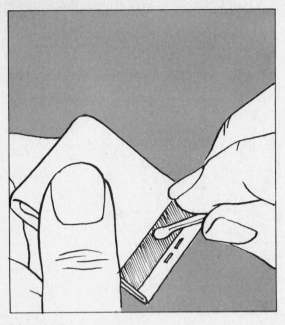

Figure E

Mechanical energy converts to heat energy.

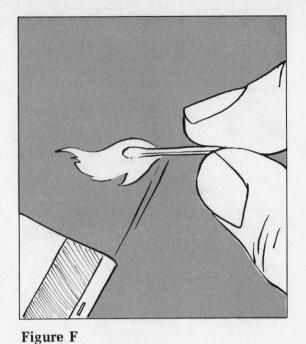

Figure F

Chemical energy converts to heat and light energy.

photoelectric cell

electric motor

Figure G

A photoelectric cell converts light energy to electrical energy.

Figure H

Someday, much of the electricity you use may come from photoelectric cells.

SOME ENERGY CONVERSIONS

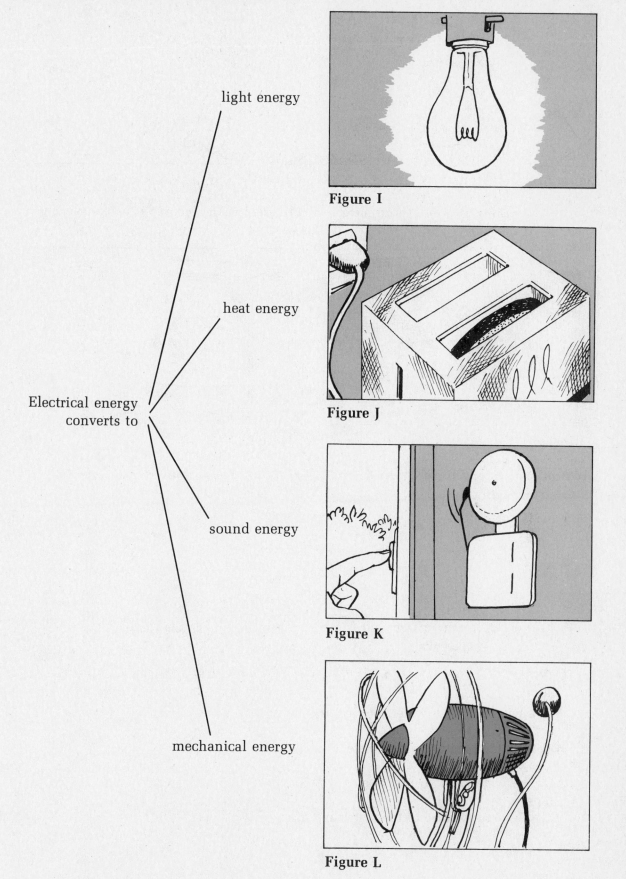

light energy

Figure I

heat energy

Figure J

Electrical energy
converts to

sound energy

Figure K

mechanical energy

Figure L

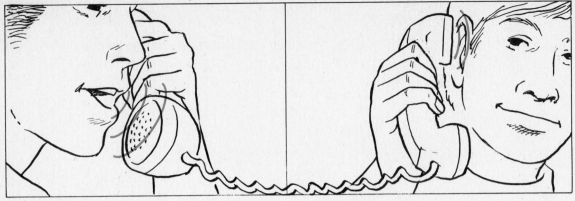

Figure M

Sound energy converts to electrical energy.

Figure N

Electrical energy converts to sound energy.

Figure O

Electrical energy converts to sound energy.

Figure P

Electrical energy converts to sound energy and light energy.

TRY THIS AT HOME!

Broken Glass

What You Need   bowl
thermometer
eggbeater

What To Do

1. Fill a bowl with tap water. Let it stand for several hours.

2. Take the temperature of the water.

3. Mix the water for two minutes with an eggbeater.

4. Take the temperature of the water again.

What You Saw; What You Learned

1. The mixing made the water temperature _____ .
   rise, drop

2. Mixing is an example of _____ energy.

3. This experiment shows that _____ energy can be converted to _____ energy.

Figure Q

COMPLETING SENTENCES Complete the sentences with the choices below. Four of these may be used more than once.

body	mechanical	atomic
electrical	conversions	chemical
change	sound	heat
light		move

1. Energy is the ability to make something _____ .

2. The main forms of energy are _____ , _____ , _____ , _____ , _____ , _____ , and _____ .

3. The energy of moving objects is called _____ energy.

4. Energy can _____ from one form to another.

5. Energy changes are called _____ .

6. Energy conversions take place inside your _____ .

7. Food has _____ energy.

8. The body changes chemical energy to _____ , _____ , and _____ energy.

9. Nerves work with _____ energy.

10. The useful energy a motor gives is _____ energy.

Match the two lists. Write the correct letter on the line next to each number.

1. _____ energy   a) has stored mechanical energy

2. _____ wound-up spring   b) has stored chemical energy

3. _____ conversions   c) energy of moving things

4. _____ mechanical energy   d) the ability to make things move

5. _____ battery   e) energy changes

WORD SCRAMBLE Unscramble each of the following to form a word or term that you have read in this Aim.

1. GYNEER   _____

2. SNOCREVNOSI   _____

3. TEAH   _____

4. DOSUN   _____

5. YELCITREICT   _____

REACHING OUT

1. Do we use *all* the energy that comes from conversions? (Hint: Think of a light bulb, or a toaster, or a car.) Explain. _____

_____

_____

2. a) What is one advantage of getting electricity from photoelectric cells?

_____

_____

b) What is one problem? _____

_____

WHAT HAPPENS TO ENERGY THAT IS NOT USED?

4

The Law of Conservation of Energy: the theory which states that energy cannot be created nor destroyed—it can only be changed

AIM 4 | What happens to energy that is not used?

Did you ever see a car overheating? Steam hisses from under the hood. The car looks like it is going to explode.

Where does all this heat come from? To answer this question we must understand some of the energy changes that take place in a car.

- Gasoline has *chemical energy*.
- Spark plugs explode the gasoline in the engine. The explosion changes the chemical energy to *heat energy*.
- The heat energy moves certain parts of the engine. This movement causes the wheels to turn. Heat energy has changed to *mechanical energy*.

CHEMICAL ENERGY $\xrightarrow{\text{converts to}}$ HEAT ENERGY $\xrightarrow{\text{converts to}}$ MECHANICAL ENERGY

Not all the chemical energy of the gasoline converts to mechanical energy. In fact, only a small amount of the chemical energy changes into energy that moves the car. The rest is waste. Some of the fuel's energy is wasted as *sound*. But most of the energy is wasted as *heat*. And this waste heat energy can overheat a car!

Some waste energy is always given off when energy changes from one form to another. Most waste energy is in the form of heat.

A car's engine releases the chemical energy of gasoline. But the energy is not used up. It just changes to other forms like mechanical, heat, and sound. THE AMOUNT OF ENERGY YOU START OUT WITH IS THE AMOUNT OF ENERGY YOU END UP WITH. ONLY THE FORMS OF ENERGY CHANGE.

We can put this idea in another way.

- Energy cannot be made.
- Energy cannot be destroyed. It is never "used up."
- Energy can just change from one form to another.

These three things are true not only in the energy of a car, but for *all* kinds of energy. Scientists call this idea the *Law of Conservation* [kon ser VAY shun] *of Energy. Conservation* means saving. Although the energy is changed, it is not lost.

WASTE ENERGY

Heat energy makes a car move. But most heat energy that comes from a gasoline engine is waste.

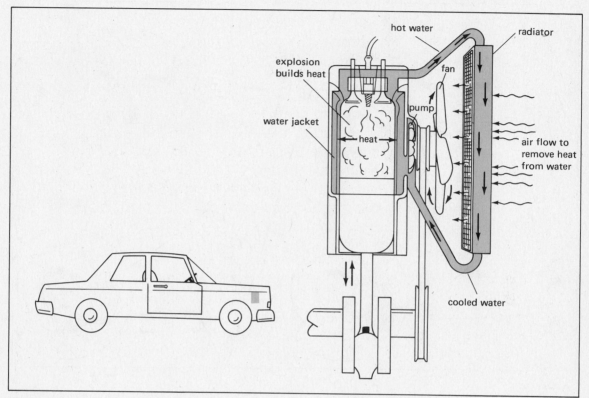

Figure A

In many cars, water keeps the engine's heat from building up. The water "picks up" the heat from the engine. The radiator then sends the heat out to the air.

Automobiles also use oil. Oil prevents the heat from wearing down moving parts.

How do cars use some of the heat

that builds up? _____

_____

Figure B

Electricity always gives off heat. Most of the time the heat is not wanted. It is waste. Sometimes the heat can be dangerous. It can cause fires.

The fuse and the circuit breaker help protect us from electrical fires. They stop the electricity from moving when too much electricity is moving in a circuit.

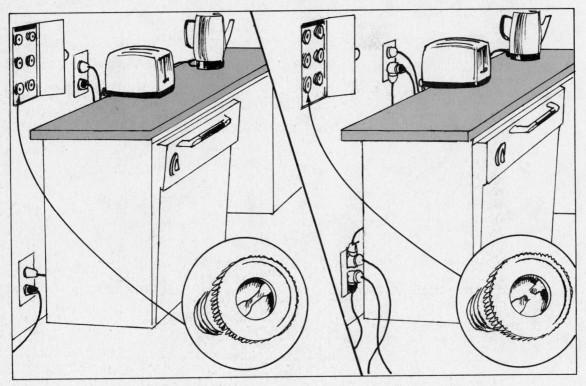

Figure C

FILL IN THE CHART

Complete this chart. Put a check (✓) in the proper box.

Six items are listed in the chart. Each item gives off heat. Is this heat used, is it wasted, or is it both—used and wasted?

	Uses Heat Produced	Wastes Heat Produced	Uses and Wastes Heat Produced
1. Toaster			
2. Fan			
3. Car			
4. Motor			
5. Electric blanket			
6. Bicycle pump			

MATCHING
Match the two lists. Write the correct letter on the line next to each number.

1. _____ matter

2. _____ energy

3. _____ heat, light, and sound

4. _____ wind and streams, for example

5. _____ potential energy

6. _____ kinetic energy

7. _____ electricity to light

8. _____ heat

9. _____ sun

10. _____ conservation

a) three forms of energy

b) stored energy

c) most waste energy is this form

d) the ability to make things move

e) saving

f) any energy in motion

g) source of most energy

h) anything that has weight and takes up space

i) an energy conversion

j) have mechanical energy

TRUE OR FALSE
Write T on the line next to the number if the sentence is true. Write F if the sentence is false.

1. _____ Heat is a form of energy.

2. _____ Heat is the only form of energy.

3. _____ Heat energy is useful.

4. _____ Heat energy is always useful.

5. _____ Energy can change from one form to another.

6. _____ Energy conversions always give off heat.

7. _____ Heat energy can change to mechanical energy.

8. _____ Mechanical energy can change to heat energy.

9. _____ A motor makes energy.

10. _____ A motor uses up energy.

WRITE IT DOWN

List the three parts of the "Law of Conservation of Energy."

Start each part with the word "Energy."

1. _____

   _____

2. _____

   _____

3. _____

   _____

WORD SEARCH

The words in this list are hidden in the groups of letters. Try to find each word. Draw a line around each. The spelling may go in any direction: up-and-down, across, or diagonally.

ENERGY
MATTER
HEAT
LIGHT
SOUND
CHEMICAL
ATOMIC
ELECTRICAL
MECHANICAL
CONVERSION

G	A	R	Y	S	T	H	G	I	L	D
R	S	E	L	O	R	O	U	A	N	N
H	G	I	L	U	S	G	C	T	T	U
E	L	E	C	T	R	I	C	A	L	O
A	H	C	O	U	N	T	C	E	M	S
T	E	T	L	A	C	I	M	E	H	C
S	R	T	H	O	T	G	S	O	T	A
M	I	C	L	I	M	O	T	U	S	E
C	E	N	E	R	G	Y	M	H	O	H
M	A	T	T	E	R	T	G	I	N	E
N	O	I	S	R	E	V	N	O	C	A

WHAT IS A FORCE?

force: a push or a pull

gravity: the earth's pull on an object

weight: the force with which an object is pulled by gravity

pound: the unit of weight in the English system

distort: to put out of shape

spring scale: a scale used to measure weight or force

AIM 5 | What is a force?

When you ride a bike, your foot *pushes* against the pedals. The push forces the wheels to turn.

When you drop something, it is *pulled* to the ground.

To turn a page, you first *pull* it up. Then you *push* it down. Try it. (At what point do you stop pulling and start pushing?)

A PUSH OR A PULL IS CALLED A FORCE. They are the only kinds of forces. We say, then, that A FORCE IS A PUSH OR A PULL.

Some forces are very weak. Others are very strong. For example, only a slight force will turn this page. More force is needed to pedal a bike. A much greater force is needed to lift heavy objects or to make a car go.

You turn a page. This is *movement*.

You pedal a bike. This is *movement*.

You pick up your books. This is *movement*, too!

We see that a force can MAKE SOMETHING MOVE.

A force can do even more. A force can also SLOW, or STOP, or CHANGE THE DIRECTION of something that is already moving. What happens to a Ping-Pong ball when you hit it with a paddle?

How do we measure forces? Forces are measured with a *spring scale*. A force distorts (changes the shape of) a spring. A push *squeezes* it. A pull *stretches* it. The number next to the arrow or line on the scale tells us how strong a force is.

A force can act in *any* direction. The force of an object that is resting or hanging freely (like a person standing or a lamp hanging from a ceiling) is called the WEIGHT of that object.

WEIGHT IS MEASURED IN POUNDS AND OUNCES in the English system of measurement.

PUSH OR PULL?

Each figure shows a *push* or a *pull*. Which one is it? Write the correct answers on spaces 1–9.

Figure A

1. _____

Figure B

2. _____

Figure C

3. _____

Figure D

4. _____

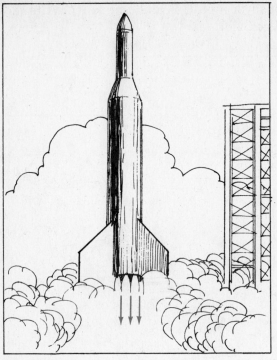

Figure E

5. _____

Figure F

6. _____

Figure G

7. _____

Figure H

8. _____

Figure I

9. _____

UNDERSTANDING THE SPRING SCALE

To understand the spring scale you must know about *gravity*. Gravity is the earth's *pull* on an object. The object's weight tells us how much the earth is pulling on it. You will learn more about gravity in the next Aim.

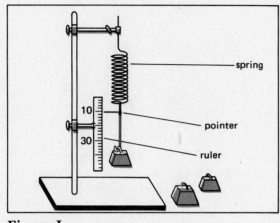

Figure J

Fill in the blanks.

1. The force of gravity is a

   _____.
      push, pull

2. A force makes the spring move

   _____.
      up, down

3. The heavier the object, the

   _____ the force.
      less, greater

4. The stronger the force, the _____ the spring stretches.
                                    more, less

5. The weaker the force, the _____ the spring stretches.
                                  more, less

6. A 1-ounce weight is a _____ force than a 2-ounce weight.
                            stronger, weaker

7. A 2-ounce force stretches a spring _____ as a 1-ounce force.
                                       twice as much, half as much

8. A 1-ounce force stretches a spring _____ as a 2-ounce weight.
                                       twice as much, half as much

9. Fill in the following chart.

Weight	Stretch
10 ounces	1 inch
20 ounces	
30 ounces	3 inches
45 ounces	
	5 inches

10. Using arithmetic and the chart above, figure out how much a 5-pound weight

    would stretch the spring. _____

FLYING

BY

PEDAL

POWER

Shortly after 8 a.m. on June 12, 1979, a large group of people stood on a beach in France. Their eyes were fixed towards the British coast, 23 miles away.

Suddenly, a shout pierced the calm air. "There it is! It's coming!" Slowly, the dot on the horizon grew larger and larger. Finally, the people could see it clearly. It was the *Gossamer Albatross* — a planelike "contraption." It looked more like a giant dragonfly than a plane.

The *Albatross* set down gently on French soil. It became the first human-powered aircraft to cross the English Channel. Its only source of energy was *pedal-power*, which turned a large rear-positioned propeller. The pilot and "motor" of the *Albatross* was Bryan Allen, a 26-year-old biochemist from California.

The trip took 2 hours and 49 minutes. During that time, Bryan pedalled without stopping, even for a moment. He didn't dare. Any pause, and the craft would have dropped into the channel. Near the half-way mark, a slight headwind slowed the *Albatross*. Its speed dropped from a steady 12 mph to a near-stalling speed of 9½ mph. Another time, the craft dropped from its

20-foot altitude to within 6 *inches* of the water. After pedalling about 1½ hours, Bryan suffered severe fatigue and dehydration. He nearly gave up. But somehow he managed to overcome his problems.

Paul MacCready also deserves high praise. He is the aerospace engineer who designed the *Albatross*.

MacCready realized that human pedal power can develop only ¼ horsepower. This tiny amount of power meant that the *Albatross* would have to be very light in weight. And its wing area would have to be very large—and especially shaped. Only then could the *Albatross* develop enough *lift* and *thrust*. Lift would push the plane *upward*; thrust would keep it moving *forward*.

MacCready used the lightest and strongest materials. The weight of the *Albatross* was kept down to about 70 pounds. So important was weight, that just before take off, the crew wiped off the dew from the wings. This water would have added a few needless pounds.

The flight of the *Albatross* was a success. MacCready and Allen and the rest of the team won a place in aviation history—

WHAT IS THE FORCE OF GRAVITY?

kilogram: 1,000 grams

mass: the amount of matter in an object

gram: the basic unit of mass measurement

AIM 6 | What is the force of gravity?

All objects pull on one another. THIS PULL IS A FORCE CALLED GRAVITY.

The earth pulls on you. The measure of how much the earth pulls on you is called your WEIGHT.

Every object has its own gravity. You have gravity. So does a piece of dust. Even a tiny atom has gravity. But these pulls are too weak to be measured. Usually a large object has a stronger gravity than a small object.

How much do you weigh? If you weigh 100 pounds, then on the moon you would weigh only 16 pounds. Why the difference? Because the moon is smaller than the earth, and therefore the moon's gravity is weaker. It would pull upon you with less force.

In outer space, you would be very *far* from both the earth and the moon. You would not feel the gravity from either one. Your weight would be *zero!* You would just float around.

Your weight changes at different gravities. But the *amount of matter* you are made of does *not* change. THE AMOUNT OF MATTER IN A SUBSTANCE IS CALLED ITS MASS.

No matter where an object is, its mass stays the same. It makes no difference how strong or how weak the gravity is —the amount of material in an object does not change.

- Gravity changes the weight of an object.
- Gravity does *not* change the mass of an object.

We see that weight and mass are different. But unless we leave the earth, the difference is not important. Therefore, we usually talk as if weight and mass were the same.

MASS IS MEASURED IN UNITS CALLED KILOGRAMS (kg). *Kilo* means one thousand. Therefore, a kilogram means 1,000 grams. A gram is a very small mass.

ON EARTH A KILOGRAM MASS EQUALS THE WEIGHT OF ABOUT 2.2 POUNDS. One ounce equals 28 grams.

In the following lessons, we will use kilograms and grams as if they were units of weight.

DIFFERENCES IN GRAVITY

Figure A shows eleven objects in the sky.

Study them. Then answer the questions.

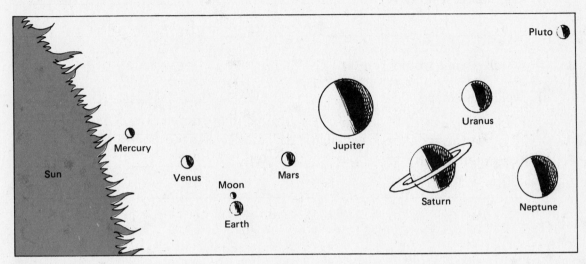

Figure A

1. Which of these:

   a) is the largest? _____

   b) is the smallest? _____

   c) has the most mass? _____

   d) has the least mass? _____

   e) has the strongest gravity? _____ Why? _____

   _____

   f) has the weakest gravity? _____ Why? _____

   _____

2. On which of these would you:

   a) weigh the most? (That's a hot question!) _____

   b) weigh the least? _____

3. Name the *planets*. _____ _____ _____

   _____ _____ _____

   _____ and _____.

4. Which are not planets? _____ _____

5. Which *planet* has

    a) the strongest gravity? _____ Why? _____

    _____

    b) the weakest gravity? _____ Why? _____

    _____

6. On which *planet* would you

    a) weigh the most? _____ Why? _____

    _____

    b) weigh the least? _____ Why? _____

    _____

THE SUN'S GRAVITY

The sun's gravity is about 28 times stronger than earth's gravity.

If you weigh 45 kilograms (100 pounds) on earth, you would weigh 1,270 kilograms (2,800 lbs.) on the sun.

Would your *mass* change on the sun? _____

Figure B

COMPLETING SENTENCES Complete the sentences with the choices below. Two of these may be used twice.

earth
small
how much gravity
more

less
large
weight

how much matter
moon
gravity

1. Mass tells us _____ an object has.

2. Weight tells us _____ pulls on an object.

3. Usually, _____ objects have stronger gravity than _____ objects.

4. The stronger the gravity, the _____ something weighs; the weaker the gravity, the _____ the weight.

5. As you move away from an object, its gravity pulls _____.

6. As you move closer to an object, its gravity pulls _____.

7. _____ does not change mass.

8. But gravity can change _____.

9. The _____ is larger than the moon.

10. The earth has greater gravity than the _____.

MATCHING Match the two lists. Write the correct letter on the line next to each number.

1. _____ weight

2. _____ mass

3. _____ large masses

4. _____ small masses

5. _____ sun

a) have strong gravity

b) measures the pull of gravity

c) gravity is 28 times that of earth

d) amount of matter in an object

e) have weak gravity

TRUE OR FALSE

Write T on the line next to the number if the sentence is true. Write F if the sentence is false.

1. _____ Mass and gravity are the same.

2. _____ On earth we usually say that mass and gravity are the same.

3. _____ Gravity changes weight.

4. _____ Gravity changes mass.

5. _____ Weak gravity makes objects heavy.

6. _____ Strong gravity makes objects heavy.

7. _____ A mass on the earth is the same on the moon.

8. _____ A weight on the earth is the same on the moon.

9. _____ A large mass usually has stronger gravity than a small mass.

10. _____ The moon's gravity is stronger than the earth's gravity.

CONNECTING DOTS

Each player draws a line. If the line completes a box, then the player goes again. Put your initials in the boxes you complete.

```
 .   .   .   .   .   .   .   .   .
 P                           E
 .   .   .   .   .   .   .   .   .
 U                           A
 .   .   .   .   .   .   .   .   .
 L       M   A   S   S       R
 .   .   .   .   .   .   .   .   .
 L                       G   T
 .   .   .   .   .   .   .   .   .
     M   O   O   N       R   H
 .   .   .   .   .   .   .   .   .
                         A
 .   .   .   .   .   .   .   .   .
 F   L   O   A   T       V
 .   .   .   .   .   .   .   .   .
                         I
 .   .   .   .   .   .   .   .   .
                         T
 .   .   .   .   .   .   .   .   .
                         Y
 .   .   .   .   .   .   .   .   .
```

Scoring:
empty box counts 1 point
box with a letter counts 2 points
add 10 points for each complete word

SCORE

Name _____ | Name _____

40

WHAT HAPPENS WHEN FORCES WORK AT THE SAME TIME?

7

resultant: the final amount and direction of a force

vector: an arrow that shows the strength and direction of a force

AIM 7 | What happens when forces work at the same time?

When you push a cart, only one force is at work—yours. If your friend helps you, a second force is added. Both forces *work together*.

In hand wrestling, two forces *push against* each other.

More than one force can work on an object at the same time. The forces can push or pull in any direction. What happens when they act depends upon two things—*how strong* the forces are, and *their directions*.

Let's study two simple examples—*opposite* forces, and forces that *work together*.

OPPOSITE FORCES Two things can happen when forces are opposite:

(a) They can *balance* each other.

(b) One force can *overpower* the other force.

Opposite forces balance each other when they have the same strength. When forces are balanced, nothing moves.

A force is overpowered when a stronger force works against a weaker force. Then the stronger force moves the weaker force.

It is easy to figure the *final* force of opposite forces. Just *subtract* the weaker force from the stronger force.

A final force and its direction is called a *resultant* [re ZUL tent].

FORCES WORKING TOGETHER Forces working together push or pull in the *same* direction. They help each other. The force becomes greater.

You find a resultant force of this kind by *adding* the helping forces.

Forces working at an angle also affect each other. But the resultant is not as easy to figure out.

WORKING WITH FORCES

The following figures show forces at work. Study each figure. Then answer the questions for each.

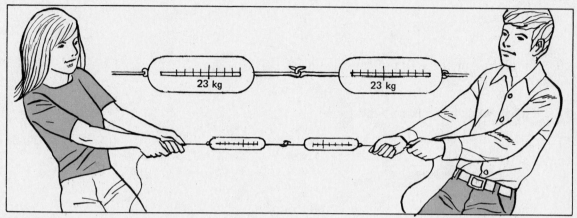

Figure A

1. The forces in Figure A are _____.
   pushing, pulling

2. The forces are _____.
   working together, working opposite to each other

3. The forces are _____.
   equal, not equal

4. The forces _____ balance each other.
   do, do not

5. The resultant force is _____.
   23 kilograms to the right, 23 kilograms to the left, zero

6. There _____ movement.
   is, is no

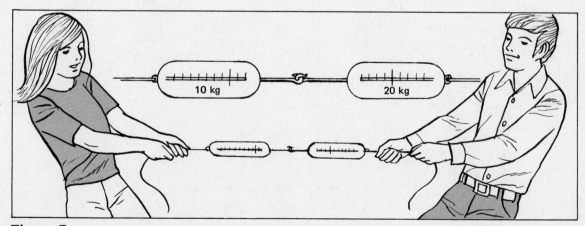

Figure B

7. The forces in Figure B are _____.
<u>pushing, pulling</u>

8. The forces are _____.
<u>working together, working opposite each other</u>

9. The forces _____ equal.
<u>are, are not</u>

10. The stronger force is pulling to the _____.
<u>right, left</u>

11. The weaker force is pulling to the _____.
<u>right, left</u>

12. There _____ movement.
<u>is, is no</u>

13. The _____ force is moving the _____ force.
<u>stronger, weaker</u>   <u>stronger, weaker</u>

14. The movement is to the _____.
<u>right, left</u>

15. The resultant force is _____.
<u>20 kilograms to the right, 10 kilograms to the left, 10 kilograms to the right, zero</u>

10 kg   20 kg

Figure C

16. The forces in Figure C are _____.
<u>pushing, pulling</u>

17. The forces are _____.
<u>working together, working opposite each other</u>

18. The forces _____ equal.

                           are, are not

19. The stronger force is pushing to the _____.

                                           right, left

20. The weaker force is pushing to the _____.

                                       right, left

21. There _____ movement.

                   is, is no

22. The _____ force is moving the _____ force.

           stronger, weaker   stronger, weaker

23. The movement is to the _____.

                                right, left

24. What is the resultant? (Remember you need a force *and* a direction.)

_____

Figure D

25. The forces in Figure D are _____.

                                    pushing, pulling, pushing and pulling

26. The forces are working _____.

                               together, opposite each other

27. a) Is there movement? _____

    b) In which direction? _____

28. What is the resultant? _____

Complete the sentences with the choices below.

overpower	help	pull
stronger	push	resultant
against	subtract	is
is no	balance	add

1. A force is a _____ or a _____.

2. Opposite forces work _____ each other.

3. Opposite forces can either _____ or _____ one another.

4. When forces are balanced, there _____ movement.

5. When one force overpowers another force, there _____ movement.

6. A final force and its direction is called a _____.

7. To find the resultant of opposite forces, you _____ the forces.

8. Forces working together _____ each other.

9. A helping force makes a force _____.

10. To find the resultant of forces working together, you _____ the forces.

HOW DO YOU SHOW A FORCE?

You show a force with a *vector* [VEK tur]. A vector is a line with an arrow. It starts with a dot.

- The dot shows where the force begins.

- The length shows the amount of force.

- The arrow shows the direction.

Figure E shows an example of a vector.

In Figure E each box stands for a force of *one kilogram*.

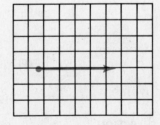

Figure E

The vector in Figure E stands for a 5 kilogram force to the *right*.

WHAT STORY DO THESE VECTORS TELL?

Fill in the chart from the information in Figure F. Each box equals a force of one kilogram.

	Force (kilograms)	Direction (right, left, up, down)
1.		
2.		
3.		
4.		
5.		
6.		
7.		
8.		
9.		
10.		

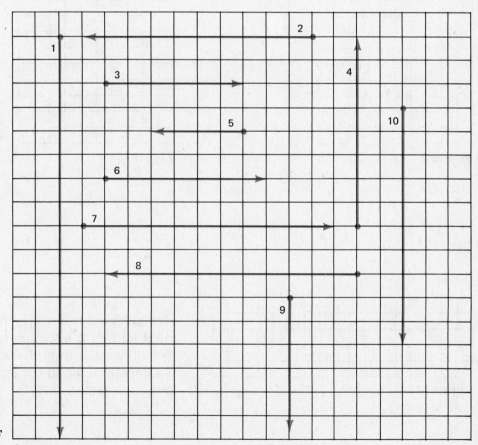

Figure F

DRAWING VECTORS

Draw each vector in the space provided. Start at the dot. Each box stands for 1 kilogram of force.

---

1. 8 kg force to the right:

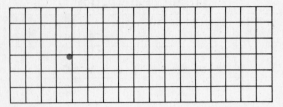

Figure G

2. 13 kg force to the left:

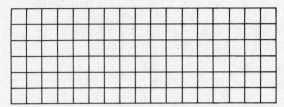

Figure H

3. 15 kg upward force:

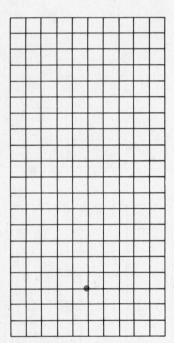

Figure I

4. 7 kg downward force:

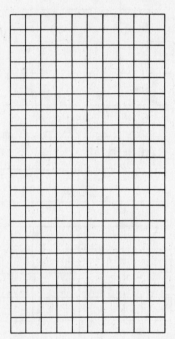

Figure J

resultant

Figure K

Figure K shows two opposite forces. There is a 5 kilogram force to the right and an 8 kilogram force to the left. We *subtract* 5 from 8. The resultant is a 3 kilogram force to the *left*. We show the resultant vector.

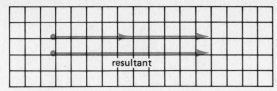

Figure L shows two helping forces. They are both 5 kilogram forces to the right. We add 5 and 5. The resultant is a *10* kilogram force to the *right*.

Figure L

DRAWING RESULTANTS

Six sets of vectors are shown below. Study each set.

Draw the resultant vector next to each set. Start at the dot. Example 1 has been done for you. (Careful, two cannot be drawn!)

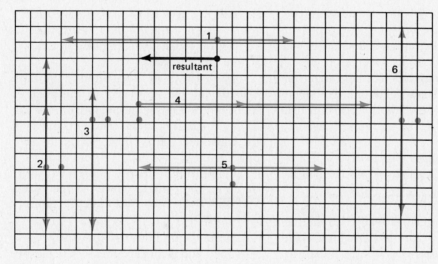

Figure M

Now fill in the chart from your work on Figure M.

	Total Number of Forces	Amount of Force (kilograms)	Direction (right, left, up, down)	Resultant	Movement? (YES or NO)
1.					
2.					
3.					
4.					
5.					
6.					

49

BASEBALL CURVES

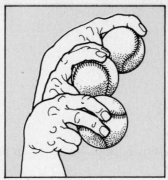
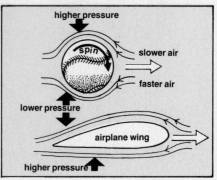

A strongly curved ball is a very effective pitch. It fools most batters seven out of ten times.

Why does a baseball curve? There are two reasons. One involves the way the ball leaves the pitcher's fingers. The other has to do with the ball's surface. It has a cowhide covering, which is held together by 216 stitches. The stitches are raised ever so slightly over the smooth covering. If it were not for these slight bumps, a baseball would not curve.

A pitcher makes a ball curve by snapping his fingers sharply across the ball as he releases it.

Suppose a ball was thrown without a spin. The air would split evenly around the ball as it moved forward. As much air would move across the top of the ball as would move across the bottom. As a result, the upward and downward air pressures on the ball would be equal. The ball would not curve.

But suppose the ball is thrown with a topspin. The raised stitches would carry a thin layer of air with them. And the air would split unevenly around the ball. This would cause air to move faster below the ball than above the ball. The faster-moving air below causes a lower air pressure than the slower-moving air above. With this difference in pressure, the ball must drop.

A baseball can be made to curve in any direction. It depends on the direction of spin the pitcher gives the ball. If he wants the ball to curve to the left, he must make the ball spin to the left. If he wants the ball to rise, he must give the ball a backspin; that is, to spin backwards.

Now think of the batter. A 90-mph fastball completes its trip to the plate in less than half a second. Good hitters can follow the ball no more than two-thirds of the way. That is for only about one quarter of a second—after that, it's guesswork.

Can a pitcher really make a ball drop or do a "right-angle curve" at the plate? Probably not—but to the batter it certainly looks that way.

It may sound strange, but throwing a curveball and flying an airplane are closely related—scientifically, that is! A baseball curves because of uneven air pressures on its surface. An airplane rises off the ground for the same reason.

Did you ever notice the shape of an airplane wing? Its top surface is curved more than its bottom surface. When a plane moves forward, air moves faster across the top surface than across the bottom surface. As with the baseball, the faster moving air causes a lower air pressure than the slower moving air. This higher air pressure on the underside of the wing pushes the plane up.

WHAT IS WORK?

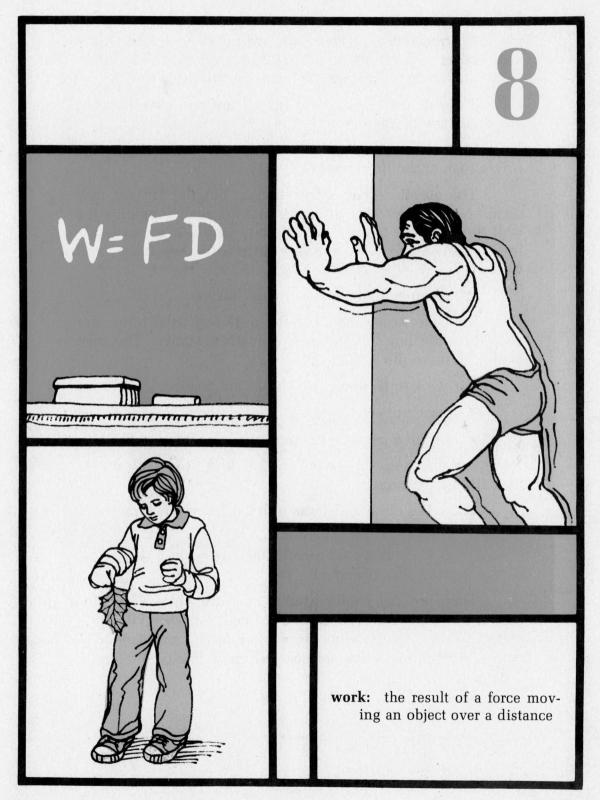

8

W= FD

work: the result of a force moving an object over a distance

AIM 8 | What is work?

A strong man pushes hard against a wall. He pushes and pushes with all his might. He huffs and he puffs. But no matter how hard he pushes, he cannot move the wall.

A small boy sees a leaf on his overalls. He flicks it away easily with one finger.

Here is a strange question: Who did more work, the strong man or the little boy?

The question may seem strange, but the answer may seem even stranger. The strong man who pushed against the wall did *no* work at all. The little boy who flicked away the leaf *did* some work. He did very little work, but it was still work.

What can explain such a strange answer?

Both the strong man and the little boy used force. But only the little boy's force made something move. The man could not make the wall move.

For work to be done, two things are needed:

- There must be a force.

- The force must make something move.

If there is no movement, no work is done—no matter how strong the force is.

There is a simple formula to help figure out how much work has been done:

$$\text{Work} = \text{Force} \times \text{Distance}$$
$$W = F \times D$$

There are many units used to measure work. Two units that measure work are the *gram-centimeter* and the *kilogram-meter*. *Gram-centimeters* measure weak forces and short distances. *Kilogram-meters* measure stronger forces and longer distances.

HOW MUCH WORK?

Figure A

This boy is pushing with a force of 15 kilograms.

The rock does not move.

How much work has the boy in Figure A done?

The formula for work is:

Work = Force × Distance

Work = 15 kilograms × 0 meters

Work = 0 (any number multiplied by zero is zero).

Force without movement means *no work is done.*

5 kilogram force

3 meter distance

Figure B

This boy has pushed a cart 3 meters. He used a force of 5 kilograms.

How much work has the boy in Figure B done?

Work = Force × Distance

Work = 5 kilograms × 3 meters

Work = 15 kilogram-meters

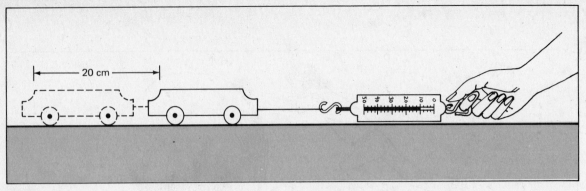

Figure C

This girl has pulled a small laboratory carriage 20 centimeters. She used a force of only 10 grams.

How much work has the girl in Figure C done?

Work = 10 grams × 20 centimeters

Work = 200 gram-centimeters

FIGURING WORK Figure the amount of work done in each example. Write your answer in the work column. Use the margin to do your arithmetic.

The first problem has been done for you.

Work	=	Force	×	Distance
10 kilogram-meters		5 kilograms		2 meters
		5 kilograms		3 meters
		5 kilograms		6 meters
		6 kilograms		5 meters
		6 kilograms		6 meters
		6 kilograms		7 meters
		10 kilograms		5 meters
		5 kilograms		20 meters
		50 grams		no distance
		200 grams		6 centimeters
		100 kilograms		30 meters

Find the *distance* in these examples. The first has been done for you.

Work	=	Force	×	Distance
20 kilogram-meters		2 kilograms		10 meters
none		10 kilograms		
100 kilogram-meters		1 kilogram		
60 gram-centimeters		3 grams		
3 gram-centimeters		60 grams		
25 kilogram-meters		5 kilograms		

Find the *force* in these examples. The first has been done for you.

Work	=	Force	×	Distance
30 kilogram-meters		2 kilograms		15 meters
150 kilogram-meters				10 meters
25 gram-centimeters				5 centimeters
120 gram-centimeters				60 centimeters
25 gram-centimeters				1 centimeter
75 kilogram-meters				75 meters

FILL IN THE BLANKS

Write the correct term in each blank to complete the sentence.

1. If the force stays the same, but the distance is longer, the amount of work is

   _____ .
   more, less

2. If the force stays the same, but the distance is shorter, the amount of work is

   _____ .
   more, less

WORD PROBLEMS Often work problems are given in sentences, not in arithmetic charts. To figure out the answers you first have to decide what you know from the sentence (the force, the distance, or the work). Then you must do the arithmetic to find the part you do not know.

1. A man lifts a 20 kilogram rock 2 meters off the ground. How much work does he

   do? _____ kilogram-meters.

2. You use a 20 kilogram force to move an object 5 meters. How much work do you

   do? _____ kilogram-meters.

3. How much work is done in lifting a 40 gram weight, 20 centimeters?

   _____ gram-centimeters.

COMPLETING SENTENCES Complete the sentences with the choices below. One of these may be used twice.

longer	short	zero
work	kilogram-meter	gram-centimeter
W = F × D	distance	force
weak	stronger	equal and opposite
push	pull	

1. Work needs two things: _____ and _____ .

2. The formula for work is _____ .

3. If there is no movement, there can be no _____ .

4. Any number multiplied by zero is _____ .

5. Two units of work are _____ and _____ .

6. Gram-centimeters measure _____ forces and _____ distances.

7. Kilogram-meters measure _____ forces and _____ distances.

8. A force is a _____ or a _____ .

9. There is no movement when two forces are _____ .

10. Forces working together make a force _____ .

HOW CAN YOU MOVE SOMETHING WITH LESS FORCE?

9

resistance: an act of working against something

friction: the rubbing of one thing against another

lubricant: something that makes things move smoothly; oil and grease are lubricants

lubricate: to apply a lubricant

AIM 9 | How can you move something with less force?

It is easy to slide on ice. Ice is smooth.

It is harder to slide on a sidewalk. A sidewalk is rough.

Everyone knows that it is easier to slide on a smooth surface than on a rough surface. But did you ever ask why?

Here is an explanation:

All surfaces have bumps and scratches. Even "smooth" surfaces have them. Smooth surfaces just have much smaller bumps and scratches than rough surfaces do. Sometimes they are so tiny you need a microscope to see them. Do you need a microscope to see a sidewalk's bumps and scratches?

When one surface moves on another surface, the bumps and scratches rub together. The rubbing is called *friction* [FRIK shun]. Friction makes movement more difficult.

Friction *resists* movement.

There is always some friction when surfaces move against one another. But the amount of friction can be greater or lesser. The rougher the surface, the greater the friction.

Friction not only builds resistance. Friction also builds heat. And heat can cause damage. That is why we try to reduce friction.

There are two main ways to reduce friction:

1. *Rolling things instead of sliding them.* Rolling friction is less than sliding friction.

2. *Lubricating* [LOO bruh kayt ing] *the surfaces of things.* Oil and grease are the most used lubricants [LOO bruh kants].

SURFACES AND FRICTION

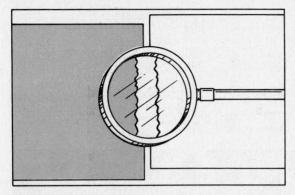

Figure A

Bumps and scratches on surfaces rub against each other and cause friction. All surfaces have bumps and scratches.

Figure B

Some surfaces have large bumps and scratches. You can see them easily.

Figure C

Some surfaces—like glass, polished wood, and metal—have tiny bumps and scratches. You cannot see them easily.

UNDERSTANDING FRICTION, RESISTANCE, AND WORK

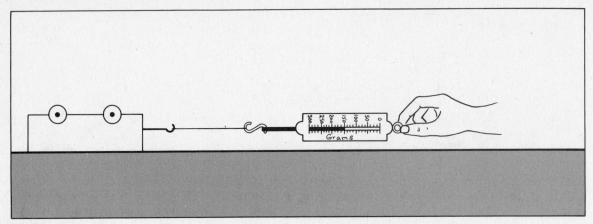

Figure D

1. How much force is pulling the laboratory carriage in Figure D? _____

2. Are the wheels in use? _____

3. This shows _____ friction.
   <u>sliding, rolling</u>

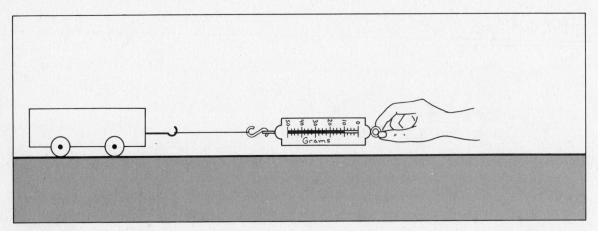

Figure E

4. **a)** Now, how much force is being used in Figure E? _____

   b) This is _____ force than was needed in Figure D.
   <u>more, less</u>

   c) Why is less force needed in Figure E? _____

   _____

5. This is an example of _____ friction.
   <u>sliding, rolling</u>

6. Rolling friction is _____ than sliding friction.
   greater, less

7. Sliding friction is _____ than rolling friction.
   greater, less

8. With sliding, there is _____ resistance than with rolling.
   more, less

9. With rolling, there is _____ resistance than with sliding.
   more, less

10. With sliding, you do _____ work.
    more, less

11. With rolling, you do _____ work.
    more, less

12. With sliding, you do more work because you use _____ force.
    more, less

13. With rolling, you do less work because you use _____ force.
    more, less

14. Which builds more heat, sliding or rolling? _____

Figure F

15. How much force is pulling the piece of wood in Figure F? _____

16. Is the surface lubricated? _____

17. Now, how much force is needed to pull the wood in Figure G? (Turn the page.)

_____

18. This is _____ force than was needed in Figure F.
    more, less

19. Why is less force needed? _____

_____

61

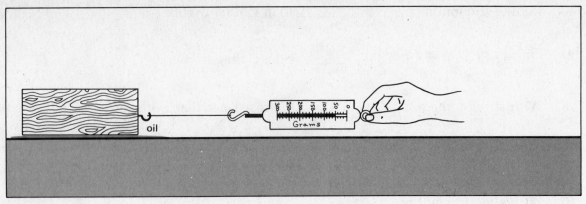

Figure G

20. Lubrication makes a surface _____ .
    rougher, smoother

21. Lubrication _____ resistance.
    increases, decreases

22. Lubrication _____ friction.
    increases, decreases

23. With lubrication you need _____ force to move an object.
    more, less

24. With lubrication, you do _____ work.
    more, less

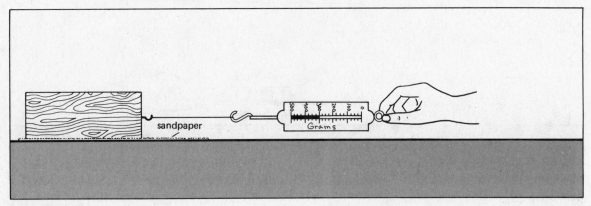

Figure H

25. How much force is needed to pull the wood in Figure H? _____

26. This is _____ force than was needed in Figure F.
    more, less

27. Why is more force needed? _____

    _____

28. Sandpaper is a _____ surface.
    rough, smooth

29. Sandpaper _____ friction.
  increases, decreases

30. On sandpaper, you need _____ force to move an object.
  more, less

31. On sandpaper, you do _____ work.
  more, less

32. Which figure shows heat building up? _____
  F only, G only, H only, all three

33. Which figure shows the most heat building up? _____
  F, G, H

FRICTION IS NOT ALL BAD

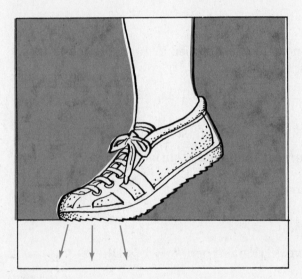

Figure I

We could not walk without friction.

Figure J

Without friction things would always be moving around.

Figure K

Car brakes would not work without friction. Why do cars slide on ice and snow?

Figure L

Sandpaper and grindstones depend upon friction.

63

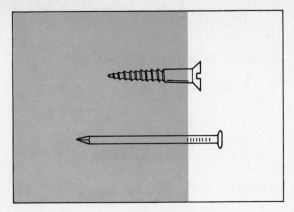

Figure M

The force of friction keeps nails and screws in wood.

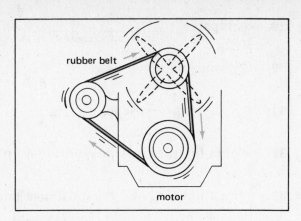

Figure N

The force of friction also keeps motor belts from slipping.

TRUE OR FALSE Write T on the line next to the number if the sentence is true. Write F if the sentence is false.

1. _____ Friction always builds heat.

2. _____ Smooth surfaces build more heat than rough surfaces do.

3. _____ Oil and grease reduce friction.

4. _____ Sand is a lubricant.

5. _____ More friction means more work. (Remember: W = F × D)

REACHING OUT

Many things work better when they are lubricated.

Name five. _____

_____

_____

_____

_____

Figure O

HOW CAN A SMALL FORCE MOVE A HEAVY OBJECT?

10

machine: any device that can change the strength of a force, its speed, or its direction

AIM 10 | How can a small force move a heavy object?

Muscles do many jobs. All day long they push and pull for you. But many jobs need more force than muscles alone can give.

For example, you can lift a spare tire from an automobile trunk. But you need a jack to lift the whole car.

A machine can make a force stronger. It can change a small force into a large force. This means that a small force can move heavy objects.

A machine can be big and complicated, or it can be simple. The most basic machines are known as *simple machines*.

There are six kinds of simple machines. They are:

- the inclined plane
- the wheel and axle
- the pulley
- the lever
- the wedge
- the screw

Most of us do not usually think of these as machines, but they are. Each one can make a force stronger. Anything that can make a force stronger is a machine.

The six simple machines can be combined in many ways to make complicated machines. If you examine a complicated machine, you will see a combination of simple machines.

Machines do not reduce the amount of work. Machines just divide work into several smaller and easier jobs. It makes no difference whether you use your muscles alone or get help from a machine. In the end, the *amount* of work you do is the same.

THE SIX SIMPLE MACHINES

Figure A   *the inclined plane*

Figure B   *the wheel and axle*

Figure C   *the pulley*

Figure D   *the lever*

Figure E   *the wedge*

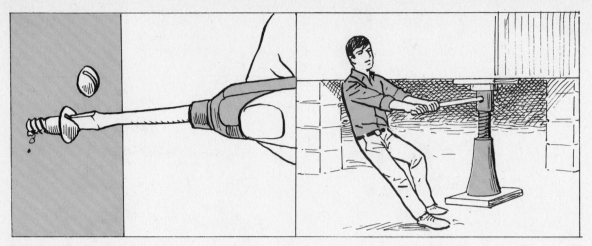

Figure F *the screw*

WHAT MACHINES DO

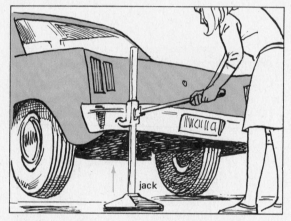

Figure G

A machine can multiply a force.

Figure H

A machine can also change direction.

Figure I

A machine can also change speed.

FILL IN THE BLANKS

A machine is any device that can _____ or _____

or _____ .

COMPLETING SENTENCES

Complete the sentences with the choices below.

easier	make a force stronger	inclined plane
screw	lever	machines
change speed	muscles	several small jobs
wedge	wheel and axle	pulley
six	work	change direction

1. Many jobs can be done only with our _____ .

2. _____ help us do very hard jobs.

3. A machine can do one or more of the following: _____ ,

   _____ , _____ .

4. There are only _____ simple machines.

5. The names of the simple machines are the _____ , the

   _____ , the _____ , the _____ , the

   _____ , and the _____ .

6. Machines do not reduce the amount of _____ .

7. Machines divide work into _____ .

8. It is _____ to do several small jobs than one big job.

TRUE OR FALSE

Write T on the line next to the number if the sentence is true. Write F if the sentence is false.

1. _____ Your muscles do work.

2. _____ Muscles can do every job.

3. _____ Machines help our muscles.

4. _____ Muscles work all machines.

5. _____ A slanted board is a machine.

6. _____ A wooden stick can be a machine.

7. _____ A machine can make a force stronger.

8. _____ One machine may be made of a combination of simple machines.

9. _____ A machine gets a job done with less work.

10. _____ A machine can only change the direction of a force.

WORD SEARCH

The words in this list are hidden in the groups of letters. Try to find each word. Draw a line around each. The spelling may go in any direction: up-and-down, across, or diagonally.

PULLEY
SCREW
WHEEL
AXLE
MACHINE
INCLINE
PLANE
LEVER
WEDGE

P	L	A	N	E	W	E	I
U	G	A	R	Y	S	D	N
L	E	E	H	W	C	G	C
L	M	I	L	S	R	E	L
E	N	I	H	C	A	M	I
Y	W	S	C	F	D	E	N
L	A	X	L	E	O	G	E
E	R	E	D	V	N	D	P
S	E	V	R	E	V	E	L
G	E	S	C	R	E	W	A

WHAT IS MECHANICAL ADVANTAGE?

11

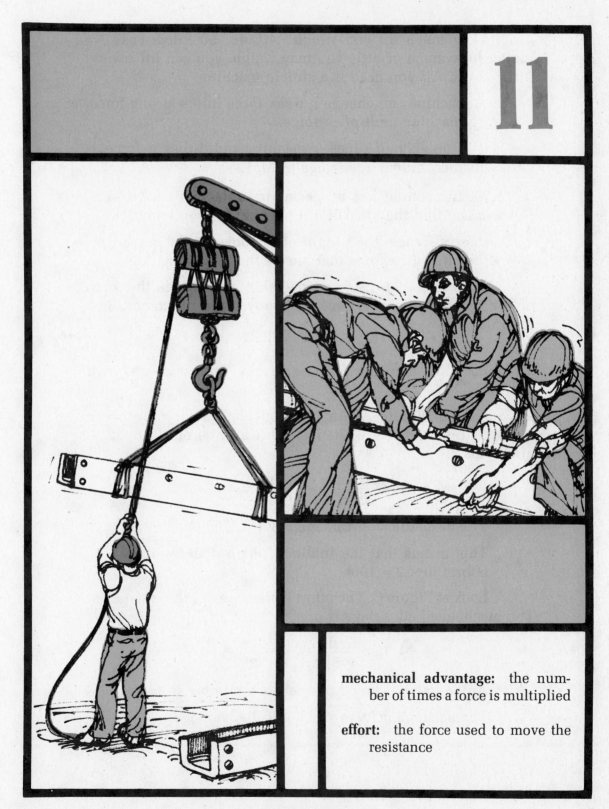

mechanical advantage: the number of times a force is multiplied

effort: the force used to move the resistance

AIM 11 | What is mechanical advantage?

How much do you weigh? 40, 45, 50 kilograms? No matter how much or little you may weigh, you can lift several *metric tons*. All you need is a simple machine.

A machine can change a weak force into a strong force. We say a machine *multiplies* force.

The number of times a machine multiplies a force is called its *mechanical advantage* or *M.A.*

Each machine has a special formula to find its M.A. But you can find the M.A. of *any* machine if you know:

the *resistance* (the weight of the object to be moved)
the *effort* (the force that moves the resistance)

To find the M.A. of any machine, you divide the force of the resistance by the force that moves the resistance. The formula is:

$$\text{M.A.} = \frac{\text{Resistance}}{\text{Effort}}$$

To understand how the formula works, let us look at two examples.

Look at Figure A. An inclined plane lets you move a 100 kilogram weight (resistance) with a force or effort of 50 kilograms.

$$\text{M.A.} = \frac{\text{Resistance}}{\text{Effort}} = \frac{100}{50} = 2$$

The mechanical advantage is 2 (M.A. = 2).

This means that the inclined plane *doubles* the effort (50 × 2 = 100).

Look at Figure C. The effort is the *same* as the resistance. The mechanical advantage is *one*.

$$\text{M.A.} = \frac{\text{Resistance}}{\text{Effort}} = \frac{25}{25} = 1$$

Any number divided by the same number is 1.

There can be no *zero* mechanical advantage.

FINDING THE MECHANICAL ADVANTAGE

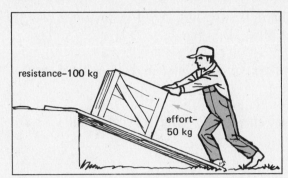

Figure A

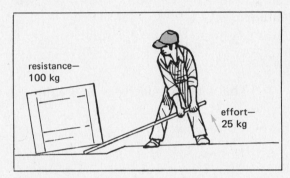

Figure B

Figure C

1. The resistance in Figure A is

   _____ kg.

2. The force (effort) is _____
   kg.

3. The force is multiplied _____
   times.

4. The M.A. is _____ .

5. The resistance in Figure B is

   _____ kg.

6. The force effort is _____ kg.

7. The force is multiplied _____
   times.

8. The M.A. is _____ .

9. The resistance in Figure C is

   _____ kg.

10. The force is _____ kg.

11. Is this machine multiplying the

    force? _____

12. The M.A. is _____ .

13. What useful job is this machine

    doing? _____

MACHINES AND MECHANICAL ADVANTAGES

Different machines have different mechanical advantages. But remember—with or without mechanical advantage, the amount of *work* is the *same*.

Machines do not reduce the amount of work. They just make the work easier to do.

A machine divides a big job into several small jobs. And several small jobs are easier to do than one big job.

FILL IN THE BLANKS   Study Figures D through F. Then fill in the blanks in the sentences next to each figure.

Figure D

1. The simple machine in Figure D is a _____.

2. The resistance is _____ kg.

3. The effort is _____ kg.

4. The effort is multiplied _____ times.

5. The M.A. is _____.

Figure E

6. The simple machine in Figure E is a _____.

7. The resistance is _____ kg.

8. The effort is _____ kg.

9. The effort is multiplied _____ times.

10. The M.A. is _____.

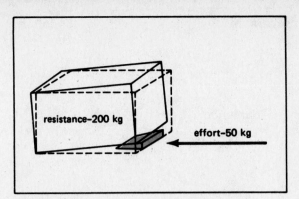

Figure F

11. The machine in Figure F is a

    _____.

12. The resistance is _____ kg.

13. The effort is _____ kg.

14. The effort is multiplied _____ times.

15. The M.A. is _____.

COMPLETING SENTENCES

Complete the sentences with the choices below.

force	more	multiplies
mechanical advantage	smaller and easier jobs	reduce work
less	resistance	easier
stronger		

1. Another name for any weight we try to move is _____.

2. The heavier the weight, the _____ the resistance.

3. The lighter the weight, the _____ the resistance.

4. A _____ is needed to move a resistance.

5. A machine makes a force _____.

6. Another way of saying this is, "A machine _____ a force."

7. The number of times a machine multiplies a force is called its _____.

8. Machines do not _____.

9. Machines just make work _____ to handle.

10. Machines divide work into _____.

Write the correct numbers in the blank places in the chart.
Remember, M.A. = $\dfrac{\text{Resistance}}{\text{Effort}}$.

	Effort	Resistance	M.A.
1.	30 kg	300 kg	
2.	5 g	25 g	
3.	15 kg	15 kg	
4.	20 kg		2
5.	2 g	100 g	
6.		200 kg	4
7.	25 kg	150 kg	
8.		150 g	5
9.	50 g	50 g	
10.	30 g		6

REACHING OUT Solve these word problems. (Hint: Figure out which numbers you are given. Solve the problem for the missing number.)

1. A 200 kg force moves an 800 kg resistance. Find the M.A. _____

2. A pulley lifts a 100 kg resistance with a force of 100 kg. Find the M.A. _____

3. The M.A. of a certain machine is 2. How much force does it use to move a 200 kg resistance? _____

4. The M.A. of a certain machine is 4. It lifts a resistance with 10 kg. What is the weight of the resistance? _____

WHAT PRICE DO YOU PAY TO GAIN MECHANICAL ADVANTAGE?

12

resistance distance: the distance the resistance moves

effort distance: the distance it takes to move the resistance

AIM 12 | What price do you pay to gain mechanical advantage?

There is a saying "You don't get anything for nothing." This may not be true for everything. But it is true for machines.

A machine does not multiply a force without "charging a price." The "price" is a greater distance the effort moves. When a machine multiplies a force, it also increases the effort distance.

To look at it another way, the less effort needed to do work, the longer the distance over which the effort must be spread. This means that the greater the mechanical advantage, the greater the distance the effort force must move.

There is a definite relationship between the effort distance and the resistance distance. For example, look at Figure A. This pulley has a mechanical advantage of 2. Using this pulley, you can lift a 50-kilogram resistance with a 25-kilogram effort force.

But in multiplying the effort force, you must increase the effort distance.

YOU MUST PULL THE ROPE 2 METERS TO MOVE THE RESISTANCE ONLY 1 METER.

Figure B shows another example. These pulleys have a mechanical advantage of 4. You need an effort force of only 20 kilograms to lift a 80-kilogram resistance.

But in multipilying the effort force, you must increase the effort distance.

YOU MUST PULL THE ROPE 4 METERS TO MOVE THE RESISTANCE ONLY 1 METER.

You have learned that a machine does not reduce the amount of work. A machine reduces the amount of effort to do work.

A machine divides a big job into smaller, easier jobs. The smaller jobs are spread out over a longer distance. If you add up the work done in all the small jobs, it is the same amount of work used to do one big job.

RESISTANCE AND EFFORT DISTANCES

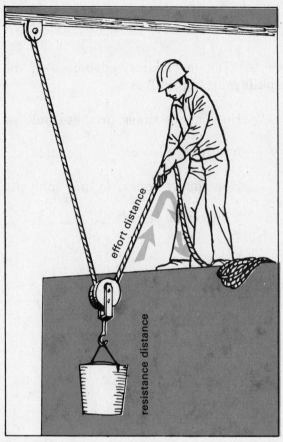

Figure A

The mechanical advantage of the pulley in Figure A is 2.

1. This pulley system multiplies the effort *force* _____ times.

2. This pulley system multiplies the effort *distance* _____ times.

How far the resistance moves is called the *resistance distance*.

How far you must pull the ropes is called the *effort distance*.

Using the pulley in Figure A, figure out how far the *effort* must move to lift a *resistance* the distances listed below.

The first one has been done for you.

Resistance Distance	Effort Distance
2 meters	4 meters
5 meters	
10 meters	
15 meters	
20 meters	
25 meters	

Now, figure out resistance distances.

Resistance Distance	Effort Distance
3 meters	6 meters
	8 meters
	12 meters
	16 meters
	40 meters
	60 meters

Figure B

The mechanical advantage of the pulleys in Figure B is 4.

3. How many times do these pulleys multiply a *force?* _____

4. How many times do they multiply a *distance?* _____

Using these pulleys, figure effort distances.

Resistance Distance	Effort Distance
2 meters	8 meters
5 meters	
10 meters	
15 meters	
20 meters	
25 meters	

Now, figure *resistance* distances.

Resistance Distance	Effort Distance
2 meters	8 meters
	12 meters
	16 meters
	40 meters
	80 meters
	100 meters

Write T on the line next to the number if the sentence is true.
Write F if the sentence is false.

1. _____ A machine makes work easier to do.

2. _____ A machine reduces the amount of work that is done.

3. _____ All machines were *invented*. (Think carefully about this one.)

4. _____ A stick can be used as a machine.

5. _____ A hill can be used as a machine.

6. _____ A machine divides a small job into several larger jobs.

7. _____ Mechanical advantage reduces effort.

8. _____ Mechanical advantage reduces distance.

9. _____ The greater the mechanical advantage, the easier the job becomes.

10. _____ The greater the mechanical advantage a pulley has, the less rope you need.

COMPLETING SENTENCES Complete the sentences with the choices below.

longer   20 meters   10 meters
mechanical advantage   distance

1. When a machine multiplies a force, it also multiplies _____.

2. The weaker the effort needed to do work, the _____ the distance over which the work is spread.

3. The greater the _____, the greater the distance.

4. If the M.A. is 2 for a pulley, you must pull the rope _____ to move the resistance 10 meters.

5. If the M.A. is 4, you must pull the rope 40 meters to move the resistance

_____.

REACHING OUT

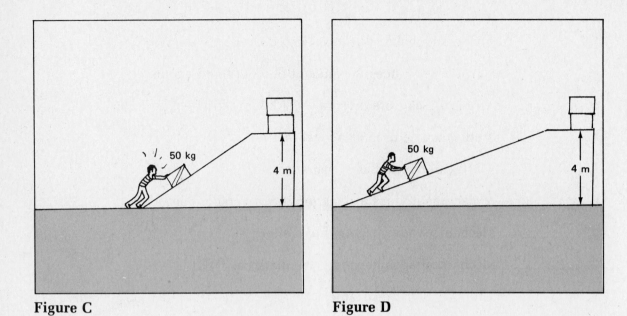

Figure C　　　　　　　　　　**Figure D**

Figures C and D show two inclined planes. A 50 kg resistance is being pushed up each incline. The boys that are pushing the resistances are equally strong.

Incline C is shorter than incline D.

You would think that the boy using incline C would reach the top sooner than the boy using incline D. But this may not be so. The boy using incline D may reach the top *before* the boy using incline C.

Can you explain why? _____

_____

_____

_____

_____

HOW DOES AN INCLINED PLANE MAKE WORK EASIER?

13

inclined plane: a slanted surface

slope:} the length of an inclined
angle:} plane compared to its
height

AIM 13 | How does an inclined plane make work easier?

What is an inclined plane?

- A plane is a *flat surface*.

- An incline is a *slant*.

- An inclined plane, then, is a *slanted flat surface*.

The inclined plane was probably the first simple machine ever used. Early cave people must have found it easier to roll heavy stones up a hill than to carry them.

Think of the things *you* do. Which is easier, walking up steep steps or up a gentle ramp? Would you rather *lift* a heavy box or *slide* it up a slanted board?

Experience has taught you that an inclined plane makes work easier.

An inclined plane multiplies force. It lets us move heavy objects with little force.

How much an inclined plane multiplies a force depends upon two things:

(a) the height of the plane
(b) the length of the plane

The length of the plane compared to its height gives a ramp its *slope* or *angle*.

An inclined plane may slope at any angle. Some slopes are gentle. Some are steep.

This is an example of an inclined plane with a *gentle* slope.

This is an example of an inclined plane with a *steep* slope.

Study Figures A, B, and C. You will see that work is easier on a gentle slope than on a steep slope.

HOW AN INCLINED PLANE MAKES WORK EASIER

You have a box that weighs 200 kilograms. You want to push it up a ramp 2 meters high. How much WORK will be done to move the box 2 meters high?

WORK = FORCE X DISTANCE

WORK = 200 kilogram X 2 meters

WORK = 400 kilogram-meters

How much FORCE is needed to do this? It all depends on the SLOPE of the ramp.

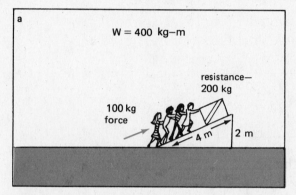

Figure A

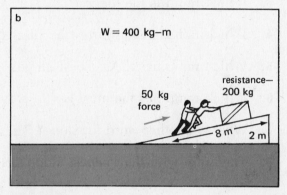

Figure B

You need a force of 100 kilograms if the ramp is 4 meters long.

This ramp multiplies a force by 2.

This means that the M.A. is 2.

You need a force of 50 kilograms if the ramp is 8 meters long.

This ramp multiplies a force by 4.

The M.A. is _____.

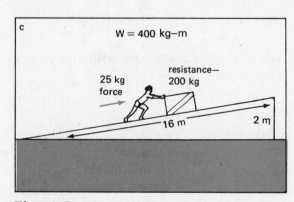

Figure C

You need a force of 25 kilograms if the ramp is 16 meters long.

This ramp multiplies force by 8.

The M.A. is _____.

Yes, an inclined plane makes work easier to do. It multiplies force. But it also multiplies distance. The weaker the force, the longer the distance over which it is used.

In the end, the *work* is the same. It makes no difference if you lift a resistance or use a ramp.

Now answer these questions by indicating Figure A, B, or C. Fill in the blanks for the other sentences.

1. Which ramp multiplies force the *most?* _____

2. Which ramp multiplies force the *least?* _____

3. Which ramp is the *longest?* _____

4. Which ramp is the *shortest?* _____

5. Which ramp has the *steepest* slope? _____

6. Which ramp has the most *gentle* slope? _____

7. What is another word for slope? _____

8. The ramp with the *steepest* slope has the _____ M.A.

largest, smallest

9. The ramp with the *gentlest* slope has the _____ M.A.

largest, smallest

10. The ramp with the *steepest* slope has the _____ distance to the top.

longest, shortest

11. The ramp with the *gentlest* slope has the _____ distance to the top.

longest, shortest

COMPLETING SENTENCES

Complete the sentences with the choices below. One of these may be used twice.

---

mechanical advantage	slant	force
sloping flat surface	does not	flat surface
length of the plane	simple machines	height
angle	slope	

1. A plane is a _____.

2. An incline is a _____ or a _____.

3. An inclined plane is a _____.

4. An inclined plane is one of the six _____.

5. An inclined plane multiplies a _____.

6. The number of times an inclined plane multiplies a force is called its

   _____.

7. The M.A. of an inclined plane depends upon two things. They are the

   _____ and its _____.

8. An inclined plane _____ reduce work.

9. An inclined plane lets you do work with less _____.

10. Another word for slope is _____.

CONNECTING DOTS

Each player draws a line. If the line completes a box, then the player goes again. Put your initials in the boxes you complete.

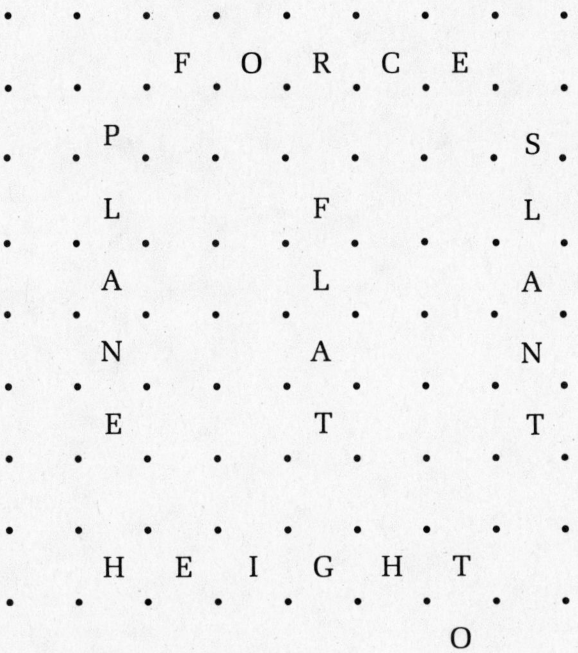

Scoring:
empty box counts 1 point
box with a letter counts 2 points
add 10 points for each complete word

FORCE

PLANE

FLAT

SLANT

HEIGHT

TOOL

RAMP

SCORE

Name _____ | Name _____

REACHING OUT

When may it be more difficult to move the *same resistance* up a gentle incline than up a steep incline? _____

_____

_____

_____

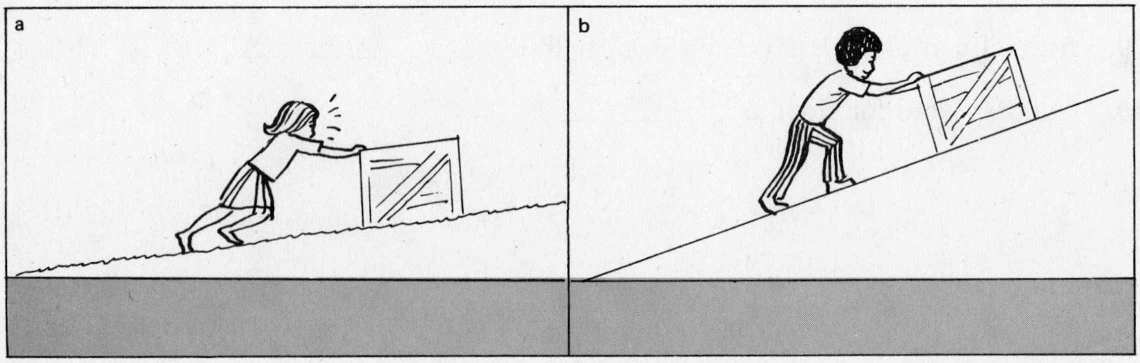

Figure D

HOW DO YOU FIGURE THE M.A. OF AN INCLINED PLANE?

14

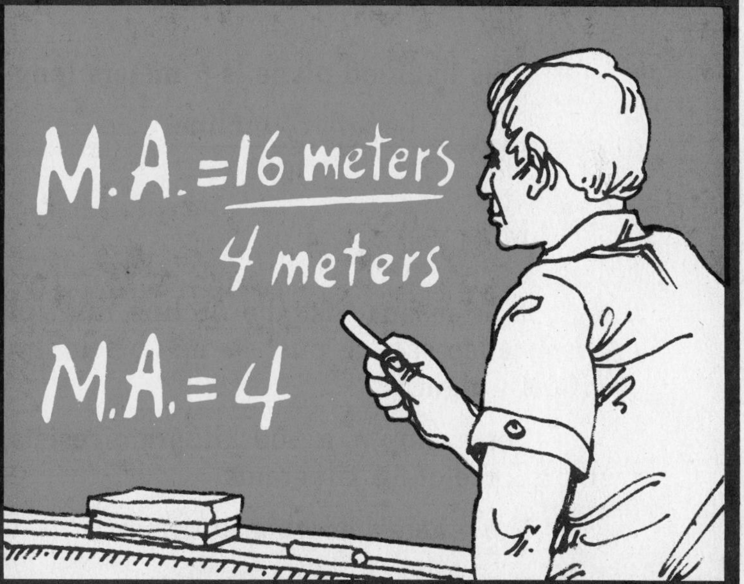

M.A. = $\dfrac{16 \text{ meters}}{4 \text{ meters}}$

M.A. = 4

M. A. of an inclined plane: the length of an inclined plane divided by the height

AIM 14 | How do you figure the M.A. of an inclined plane?

Can you divide four by two, or nine by three? Of course you can! Then you can figure the mechanical advantage of an inclined plane.

To find the M.A. of an inclined plane, just divide the height into the length of the incline.

$$M.A. = \frac{\text{Length of incline}}{\text{Height}}$$

Let's try an example.

This inclined plane is 6 meters long and 3 meters high.

$$M.A. = \frac{\text{Length of incline}}{\text{Height}}$$

$$M.A. = \frac{6}{3} = 2$$

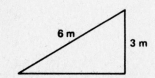

This means that the incline multiplies a force by two. A resistance can be pushed up this incline with a force *one half* its weight.

For example, a 100 kilogram resistance can be pushed with a force of 50 kilograms.

Now, here's another example.

This inclined plane is 12 meters long and 3 meters high.

$$M.A. = \frac{\text{Length of incline}}{\text{Height}}$$

$$M.A. = \frac{12}{3} = 4$$

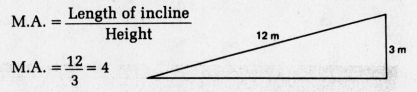

This means that the incline multiplies a force *four* times. A resistance can be pushed up this incline with a force just *one-fourth* its weight.

For example, a 100 kilogram resistance can be pushed with a force of only 25 kilograms.

Study each incline in Figures A and B. Then fill in the blanks and the charts.

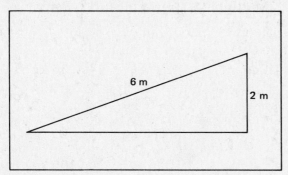

Figure A

1. In Figure A, the mechanical advantage is _____.

2. A force is multiplied _____ times.

    How much *force* will move each of these resistances? (The first one has been done for you.)

Resistance	Force
15 kg	5 kg
30 kg	
39 kg	
120 kg	
150 kg	

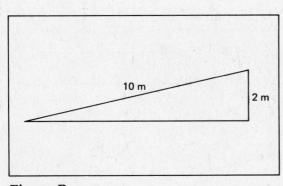

Figure B

3. In Figure B, the mechanical advantage is _____.

4. A force is multiplied _____ times.

    How much *resistance* will each of these forces move? The first one has been done for you.

Resistance	Force
50 kg	10 kg
	25 kg
	40 kg
	100 kg
	125 kg

COMPLETE THIS CHART

	Length of Incline	Height	M.A.	Number of Times The Force Is Multiplied	Resistance	Force
1.	10 meters	5 meters			100 kg	
2.	50 meters	10 meters				30 kg
3.	30 meters	6 meters			60 kg	
4.	90 meters	30 meters			75 kg	
5.	100 meters	25 meters				100 kg

FIND THE M.A. OF EACH OF THESE INCLINES

Use a metric ruler to measure the important lines. Then figure the M.A.

1.

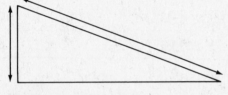

Figure C

Incline = _____ cm

Height = _____ cm

M.A.　 = _____

2.

Figure D

Incline = _____ cm

Height = _____ cm

M.A.　 = _____

3.

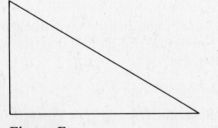

Figure E

Incline = _____ cm

Height = _____ cm

M.A.　 = _____

4.

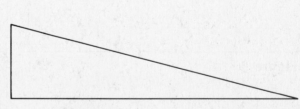

Figure F

Incline = _____ cm

Height = _____ cm

M.A.　 = _____

92

1. The number of times a machine multiplies a force is called its
   a) mechanical ability
   b) mechanical disadvantage
   c) mechanical advantage

   1. _____

2. A mother is pushing a baby carriage. The carriage is the
   a) effort
   b) resistance
   c) work

   2. _____

3. In pushing the baby carriage, the mother's force is the
   a) effort
   b) resistance
   c) work

   3. _____

4. A *plane* is
   a) flat
   b) curved
   c) a simple machine

   4. _____

5. Another word for incline is
   a) plane
   b) angel
   c) angle

   5. _____

6. An *incline* is
   a) straight with the ground
   b) at an angle with the ground
   c) always steep

   6. _____

Figure G   **Figure H**   **Figure I**

7. Three inclined planes are shown in Figures G, H, I. Which one has the *steepest* slope?
   a) G
   b) H
   c) I

   7. _____

8. Which of the inclined planes in Figures G, H, and I gives the *greatest* mechanical advantage?

    a) G

    b) H

    c) I

8. _____

9. Which of these inclined planes gives the *least* mechanical advantage?

    a) G

    b) H

    c) I

9. _____

10. Which of these inclined planes makes work easiest?

    a) G

    b) H

    c) I

10. _____

CROSSWORD PUZZLE

Fill in the blank spaces by following the clues across and down.

Across

1. What a machine does to a force

5. A push or a pull

6. To take in food

7. A point

8. A metal

9. An inclined plane

11. Thing used for writing

Down

2. Slant

3. Musical sound

4. A direction

5. Hi-_____ (stereo)

7. A spinning toy

10. Self

HOW IS A WEDGE LIKE AN INCLINED PLANE?

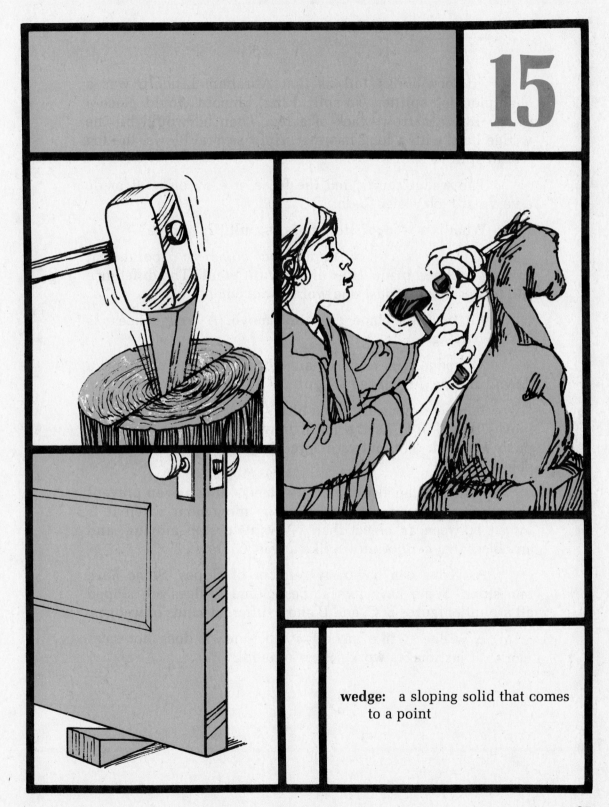

15

wedge: a sloping solid that comes to a point

History books tell us that Abraham Lincoln was a champion log splitter. To split a log, Lincoln would place a *wedge* into a narrow crack of a log. Then he would hit the wedge hard with a long hammer. After several blows, the log would split in two.

The wedge multiplied the force of each blow. It made a very hard job easier to do.

What is a wedge? How does it multiply a force?

A wedge is a sloping solid that comes to a point. But so is an inclined plane. How are they different? The difference can be described in just one word—*movement*.

An inclined plane does *not* move. A wedge does its job by *moving*.

A wedge can work in any direction. Let us study a *downward-moving wedge* (Figure A).

When a downward force hits against a wedge, the point moves *downward*. As the point moves downward, the sides push *outward*. The outward force is very great. It can split objects.

A wedge can also *lift* heavy objects. It can even *prevent* objects from moving. A wedge stops movement when it is forced between an object that we want to stop moving, and an object that *cannot* move, like a wall or floor.

A wedge can have any number of slopes. Some have one slope. Some have two slopes. Some wedges are sloped all around. Figures B, C, and D show different kinds of wedges.

A wedge is like any other machine. It does not save work. It just makes work easier to handle.

HOW A WEDGE WORKS

Figure A shows a wedge with a *downward* force.

A force moves the point *downward*. As the point moves downward, the sides push *outward*.

The outward force is *very* great. It is the downward force multiplied several times.

Figure A

WEDGE SLOPES

Some wedges have *one* slope.

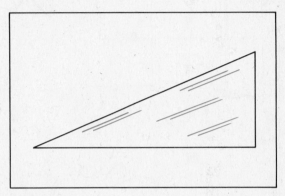

Figure B

Some wedges have *two* slopes.

This is like two inclined planes back to back.

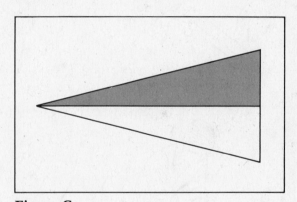

Figure C

Some wedges are sloped *all around*.

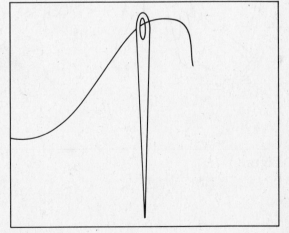

Figure D

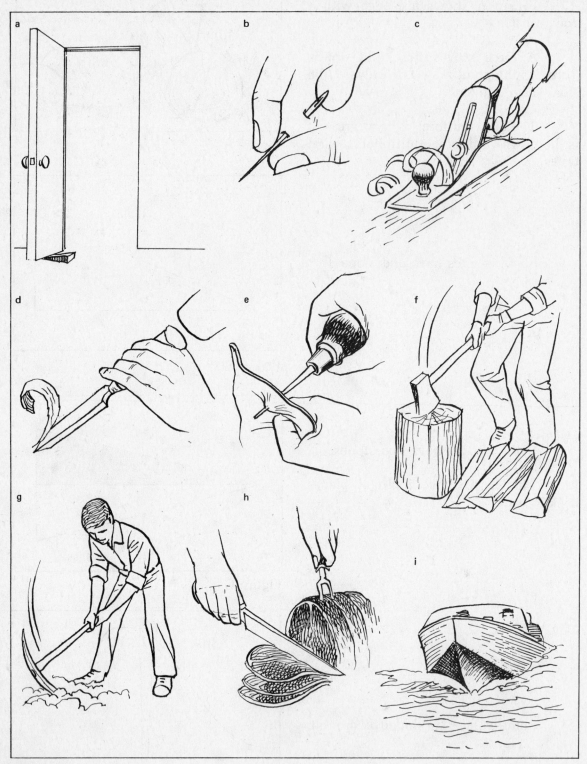

Figure E

How many can you identify?

COMPLETING SENTENCES

Complete the sentences with the choices below.

back-to-back	simple machines	point
sloping solid	distance	inclined planes
easier	reduce	stronger
any number	moves	does not move
the same		

1. A wedge is one of the six _____.

2. A machine can make a force _____.

3. A machine does not _____ work.

4. A machine makes work _____ to handle.

5. A machine multiplies a force. But it also multiplies _____.

6. With or without a machine, the work is _____.

7. A wedge is a _____ that comes to a _____.

8. The difference between an inclined plane and a wedge is that an inclined plane _____. A wedge _____.

9. A wedge may have _____ of slopes.

10. A wedge with two slopes is like two _____ that are _____.

DRAWING WEDGES

1. Draw a wedge with a single, *gentle* slope.

Figure F

2. Draw a wedge with a single, *steep* slope.

Figure G

Match the two lists. Write the correct letter on the line next to each number.

1. _____ to make work easier
2. _____ moves objects and prevents objects from moving
3. _____ inclined plane
4. _____ wedge
5. _____ mechanical advantage

a) jobs of a wedge

b) does not move

c) the number of times a force is multiplied

d) main job of machines

e) helps work by moving

THROW ONE OUT In each of the following sets of terms, one of the terms does *not* belong. Circle that term.

1. machines   make work easier   make work more difficult

2. wedge   any number of slopes   only one or two slopes

3. does not move   moves   inclined plane

4. wedge   does not move   moves

5. $\dfrac{\text{length of incline}}{\text{height}}$ $\dfrac{\text{height}}{\text{length of incline}}$ finds M.A. of inclined plane

REACHING OUT

1. A rocket is shaped like a simple machine. Name this simple machine. _____

2. Why is a rocket shaped this way?

_____

3. You know other moving things that are shaped this *general* way. Name some of them. _____

_____

Figure H

100

HOW IS A SCREW LIKE AN INCLINED PLANE?

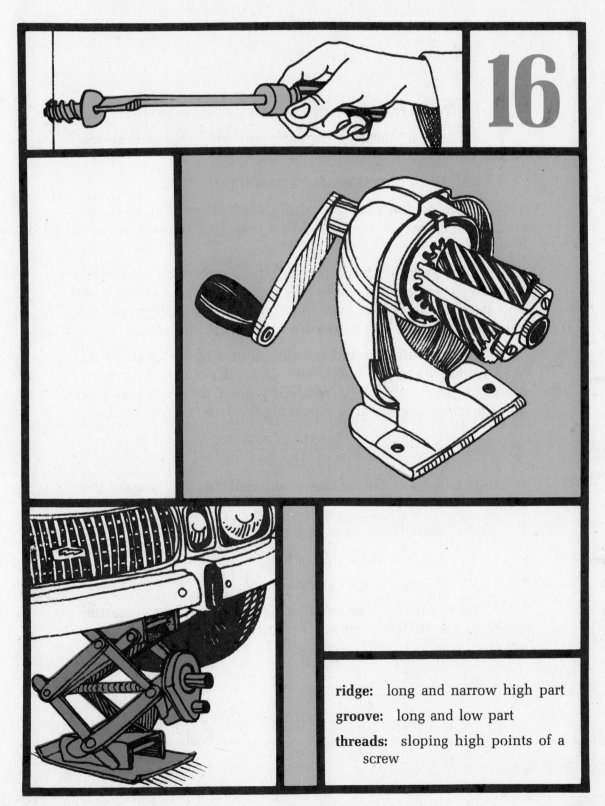

ridge: long and narrow high part

groove: long and low part

threads: sloping high points of a screw

Look at Figure A and try this simple experiment:

(a) Cut a piece of paper in the shape of a long triangle (1).

(b) Now wrap it around a pencil (2).

Examine the paper carefully (3). Notice that it winds around the pencil at an *angle*. What does it look like? Doesn't it remind you of a screw?

What you have made is really the idea behind the screw. A screw is an inclined plane that spirals around a metal rod. The winding forms *grooves* (low points), and *ridges* (high points) (Figure B). The ridges are also called *threads*.

If you could unwind the thread of a screw, you would have a very long inclined plane. It is *especially* long compared to the height of its rod. This great difference in size gives a screw a very large mechanical advantage. Remember,

$$\text{M.A.} = \frac{\text{Length of incline}}{\text{Height}}.$$

The longer the incline compared to the height, the greater the M.A.

The screw helps us in two ways:

(1) A screw holds things together.

(2) A screw raises heavy objects.

But a screw is like any machine. It does not reduce the amount of work. It just makes work easier to handle.

THE SCREW

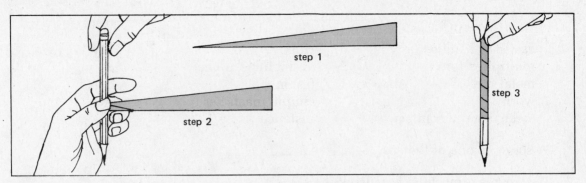

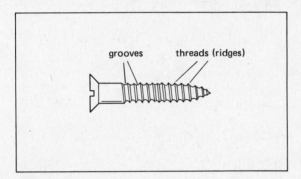

Figure A *The wound paper shows grooves and ridges. So does a screw.*

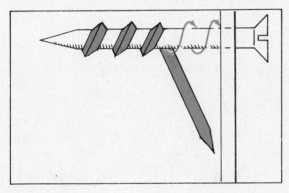

Figure B

A household screw

Figure C

If a screw could be "unwound," we would see a long inclined plane.

A screw multiplies a force. But it also multiplies distance. Take the jack screw in Figure D for example. You must turn the screw a lot in order to raise the resistance a little bit.

Figure D

COMPLETING SENTENCES

Complete the sentences with the choices below.

easier to handle	ridges	very long
multiplies force	an inclined plane	lift
metal rod	fasten	threads
work	simple machines	force
mechanical advantage	distance	

1. A screw is one of the six _____.

2. A screw is a machine because it _____.

3. A screw is really _____ wound around a _____.

4. The spiral of a screw usually is _____ compared to its height.

5. A long spiral gives a screw a large _____.

6. The high points of a screw are called the _____ or _____.

7. Screws do two kinds of jobs. They _____ and _____.

8. A screw is like any other machine. It multiplies _____ as *well* as _____.

9. A machine does not reduce the amount of _____.

10. A machine makes work _____.

MATCHING

Match the two lists. Write the correct letter on the line next to each number.

1. _____ machines   **a)** a simple machine

2. _____ screw   **b)** high points of a screw

3. _____ grooves   **c)** make work easier

4. _____ ridges   **d)** large M.A.

5. _____ long incline compared to height   **e)** low points of a screw

STUDYING SCREWS

Two screws are shown in Figures E and F. The lengths are the same. But the threads are different.

Study each screw. Then answer the questions and fill in the blanks.

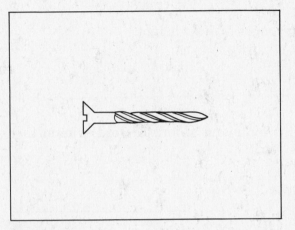

Figure E

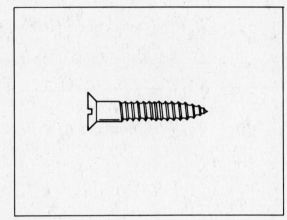

Figure F

1. Which screw . . .

   a) has more threads? _____

   b) has fewer threads? _____

   c) has the larger M.A.? _____

   d) has the smaller M.A.? _____

   e) will take more turns to attach? _____

   f) will take fewer turns to attach? _____

2. Which thread angle

   a) is steeper? _____

   b) is less steep? _____

3. The steeper the thread angle, the _____ the inclined plane.

longer, shorter

4. The more gentle the thread angle, the _____ the inclined plane.

longer, shorter

5. The steeper the thread angle, the _____ the M.A.

greater, less

6. The more gentle the thread angle, the _____ the M.A.

greater, less

Write T on the line next to the number if the sentence is true.
Write F if the sentence is false.

1. _____ A screw is like a winding inclined plane.

2. _____ A screw does its job by moving.

3. _____ All screws give the same M.A.

4. _____ The thread of every screw is longer than its height.

5. _____ Screws only hold things together.

WORD
SCRAMBLE Unscramble each of the following to form a word or term that
you have read in this Aim.

1. DHEART _____

2. VORGOE _____

3. WRECS _____

4. RIPLAS _____

5. NICLEIN _____

HOW DOES A PULLEY MAKE WORK EASIER?

block and tackle: a group of pulleys

fixed: not movable

AIM 17 | How does a pulley make work easier?

Did you ever raise or lower a window blind? If you have, you have used a *pulley*.

When you raise a blind, does the cord move up or down? When you lower a blind, does the cord move up or down?

Is there anything in your classroom that works the same way?

Pulleys can do two kinds of jobs.

(a) Pulleys can change the direction of the effort.

(b) Pulleys can also multiply the effort force.

There are three kinds of pulleys: the *single fixed pulley*, the *single movable pulley*, and the *block and tackle*.

■ The *single fixed pulley* does not multiply force. It has an M.A. of *one*. A single fixed pulley just changes the direction of a force.

■ The *single movable pulley* multiplies a force by *two* (M.A. = 2). It *doubles* a force. But it does not change the direction of a force.

■ The *block and tackle* is a *system* of pulleys. Some pulleys in the system move. Some do not. A block and tackle multiplies a force many times. It is used to raise very heavy objects. A block and tackle also changes the direction of a force.

It is easy to figure the mechanical advantage of a pulley. Just count the number of strands holding up the *weight*. This number is the same as the mechanical advantage. For example, if 3 strands are holding up a resistance, then the M.A. is 3.

When you count the pulley strands, you do *not* count the strand that is being pulled. *There is one exception.* On a single movable pulley, you count *all* the strands. (There are two).

Pulleys that multiply force do not reduce the amount of work. They just make work easier to handle.

WHAT IS A PULLEY?

A pulley is a grooved wheel that turns on a rod called an *axle*.

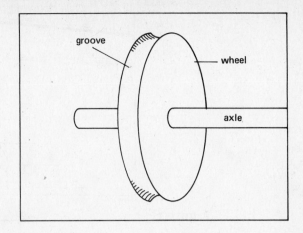

Figure A

A *fixed* pulley *does not* move up and down.
A *movable* pulley *does* move up and down.

Two pulleys are shown in Figures B and C. Study each one. Then fill in the blanks to go with each figure.

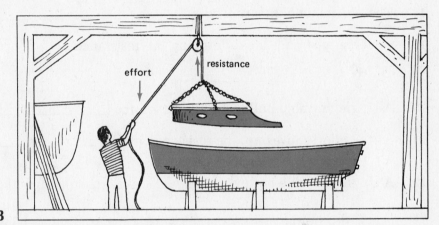

Figure B

1. The pulley in Figure B _____ move.
   <small>does, does not</small>

2. A pulley that does not move is called a _____ pulley.

3. The *full* name of this pulley is _____.

4. How many strands are holding up the resistance? _____

5. The M.A. is _____.

6. A single fixed pulley _____ multiply a force.
   <small>does, does not</small>

7. As the effort moves down, the resistance moves _____.
   <small>up, down</small>

8. What useful job does a single fixed pulley do? _____

_____

9. Using this pulley, you need a force of _____ to lift a 50 kilogram resistance.

Figure C

10. The pulley in Figure C _____ move.
    <small>does, does not</small>

11. A pulley that moves is called a _____ pulley.

12. The *full* name of this pulley is _____.

13. How many strands are holding up the resistance? _____

14. The M.A. is _____.

15. A single movable pulley multiplies a force _____ times.

16. As the effort moves up, the resistance moves _____.
    <small>up, down</small>

17. A single movable pulley _____ change direction.
    <small>does, does not</small>

18. Using this pulley, you need a force of _____ to lift a 50 kilogram resistance.

BLOCK AND TACKLE

1. Figure D shows a pulley *system*.
   It is called a _____.

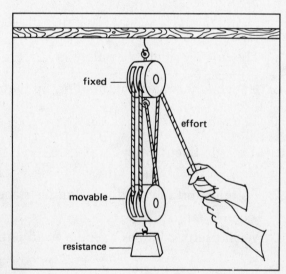

Figure D

2. Each wheel is considered a pulley.

    a) How many *fixed* pulleys does this block and tackle have? _____

    b) How many *movable* pulleys does it have? _____

3. How many strands are holding up the resistance? _____

4. The M.A. is _____.

5. This block and tackle multiplies a force _____ times.

6. It _____ change the direction of the force.
        _{does, does not}

7. Using this block and tackle, how much force would you need to lift each of these resistances?

    a) 100 kilograms _____

    b) 200 kilograms _____

    c) 400 kilograms _____

    d) 1000 kilograms _____

PULLEYS MULTIPLY DISTANCE

A pulley is like any other machine. It multiplies force. But it also multiplies *distance*.

Take a single movable pulley for example (M.A. = 2). For every *one* meter you lift the resistance, you must pull the rope *two* meters.

In the end, the work done is the same—with or without the pulley.

Figure E

111

FIGURING MECHANICAL ADVANTAGE

What is the M.A. of each of these pulleys or pulley systems?

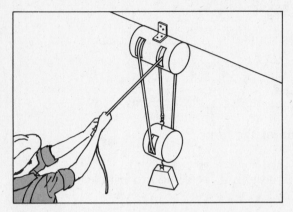

Figure F

1. M.A. = _____

Figure G

2. M.A. = _____

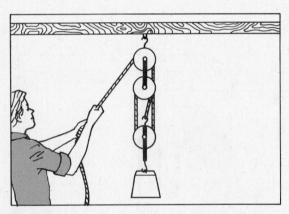

Figure H

3. M.A. = _____

Figure I

4. M.A. = _____

MATCHING Match the two lists. Write the correct letter on the line next to each number.

1. _____ single movable pulley

2. _____ block and tackle

3. _____ single fixed pulley

4. _____ M.A. of most pulleys

a) the number of strands minus one

b) used to lift very heavy objects

c) M.A. of 2

d) only changes the direction of a force

HOW DOES A WHEEL AND AXLE MAKE WORK EASIER?

18

axle: a shaft

diameter: a line that goes through the center of a circle; it passes from one edge of a circle to the other

millimeter (mm): a measurement of distance; one thousandth of a meter

AIM 18 | How does a wheel and axle make work easier?

Every time you turn a doorknob, you use a machine. A doorknob is part of a *wheel and axle*. The knob is the *wheel;* the thin shaft connected to the knob is the shaft or *axle* (Figure B).

The knob makes it easy to turn the axle.

Think of your own experiences. Did you ever try to open a door that had a missing knob? Was it easy or difficult to turn the shaft?

A wheel and axle multiplies a force. It builds a small force into a larger force.

The amount a wheel and axle multiplies a force depends upon two things:

(a)   the diameter of the wheel, and

(b)   the diameter of the axle.

How do you find the mechanical advantage of a wheel and axle? It is easy. Just divide the diameter of the wheel by the diameter of the axle.

Look at Figure C for example. The diameter of the wheel is 40 centimeters. The axle is 10 centimeters in diameter. The mechanical advantage, then, is 4.

$$M.A. = \frac{\text{Diameter of wheel}}{\text{Diameter of axle}}$$

$$M.A. = \frac{40 \text{ cm}}{10 \text{ cm}} = 4 \qquad M.A. = 4$$

But a wheel and axle is like any other machine. What it adds in M.A., it loses in the distance the effort has to move.

The wheel and axle is also like any machine. It does not reduce the amount of work. It just makes work easier to handle.

WHAT IS A DIAMETER?

A *diameter* is a line that passes through the center of a circle. It passes from one part of the circle to the opposite part.

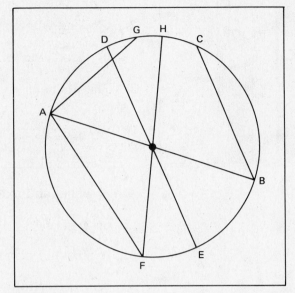

Figure A

Some of the lines within the circle in Figure A are diameters. Some are not.

Study the lines. Then put a check (√) in the proper box.

Line	Is a Diameter	Is Not a Diameter
AB		
AG		
BC		
FH		
AF		
DE		

Now fill in the answer to these questions.

1. Measure the lines that are *diameters*. How long *is each* one? _____

2. Are they all the same length? _____

3. In any one circle, the diameters are the _____ length.

115

WHICH IS WHICH?

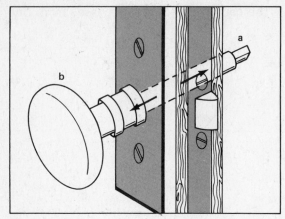

Figure B

1. A *complete* door knob is a simple machine called a _____.

2. **a)** The wheel is labeled _____.

   b) The axle is labeled _____.

3. The diameter of the wheel is

   _____ than the diameter

   larger, smaller

   of the axle.

4. A wheel and axle is a machine because it _____ a force.

5. A machine may multiply a force. But it also multiplies _____.

FINDING MECHANICAL ADVANTAGE

A wheel and axle is like any other machine. It multiplies force. But, it also multiplies *distance*.

Look at the wheel and axle in Figure C, for example. It multiplies a force 4 times. But to raise a resistance just 20 *centimeters*, you must turn the large wheel *80 centimeters*.

The mechanical advantage of this wheel and axle is 4.

1. Keeping the axle at 10 cm, what would the M.A. be with a

   a) 30 cm *wheel?* _____

   b) 50 cm *wheel?* _____

2. Keeping the wheel at 40 cm, what would the mechanical advantage be with a

   a) 5 cm *axle?* _____

   b) 20 cm *axle?* _____

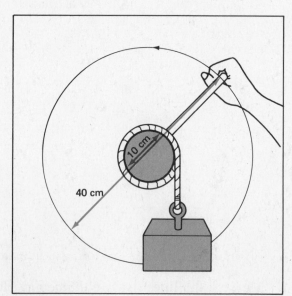

Figure C

MEASURING DIAMETERS

Four wheels and axles are shown below.

Measure the wheel and axle of each one with your metric ruler. (Use the mm measurements.)

Then figure the M.A. for each.

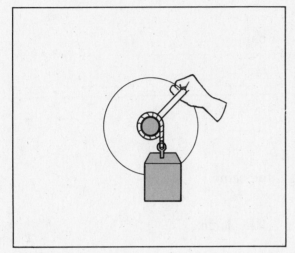

Figure D

1. Wheel diameter = _____ mm

   Axle diameter = _____ mm

   M.A. = _____

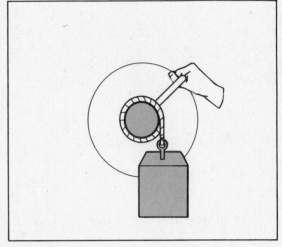

Figure E

2. Wheel diameter = _____ mm

   Axle diameter = _____ mm

   M.A. = _____

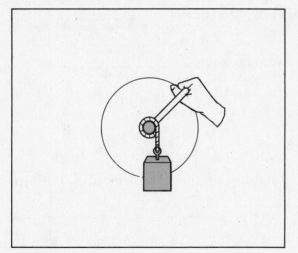

Figure F

3. Wheel diameter = _____ mm

   Axle diameter = _____ mm

   M.A. = _____

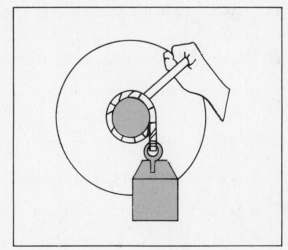

Figure G

4. Wheel diameter = _____ mm

   Axle diameter = _____ mm

   M.A. = _____

FINDING THE M.A. OF WHEELS AND AXLES

Find the mechanical advantage of each of these wheels and axles. Then fill in the blanks below.

	Wheel Diameter	Axle Diameter	M.A.
1.	20 cm	2 cm	
2.	22 cm	2 cm	
3.	26 cm	2 cm	
4.	30 cm	2 cm	
5.	38 cm	2 cm	

6. In the examples in the chart,

   a) the axle diameters _____ the same.
   are, are not

   b) the wheel diameters _____ the same.
   are, are not

7. The largest M.A. is the one with the _____ wheel.
   largest, smallest

8. The smallest M.A. is the one with the _____ wheel.
   largest, smallest

9. To gain more M.A. you use a larger _____.
   axle, wheel

10. If you were to use a *thicker axle*, the M.A. would become _____.
    larger, smaller

11. If you were to use a *thinner axle*, the M.A. would become _____.
    larger, smaller

REACHING OUT

A wheel and axle is a simple machine. But it has another simple machine built-in.

Which one is it? _____

WHAT DO YOU CALL THE PARTS OF A LEVER?

fulcrum: the point on which a lever rests

resistance arm: the distance between a fulcrum and a resistance

effort arm: the distance between a fulcrum and an effort

AIM 19 | What do you call the parts of a lever?

Did you ever pry a lid from a can? If you did, you have used a *lever*.

A lever can multiply a force many times. It lets you do tough jobs that you cannot do with your muscles alone. A lever also changes the direction of a force.

Figure A shows a lever. Look at it.

A lever has two main parts:

(1) a *rod* or *plank* that is free to turn

(2) a steady point for the plank to rest and turn upon. We call this steady point the *fulcrum* [FULL krum].

A *resistance* rests on one side of the fulcrum. An *effort* presses on the other side. The effort is the force needed to *move* the resistance.

The distance between the fulcrum and resistance is called the *resistance arm* or *resistance distance*.

The distance between the fulcrum and effort is called the *effort arm* or *effort distance*.

You can change the resistance distance and effort distance by changing the fulcrum. When the fulcrum changes, the M.A. changes too.

STUDYING THE LEVER

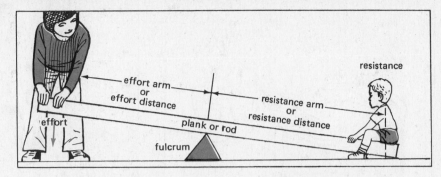

Figure A

The parts of a lever

Four levers are shown in Figures B through E. In each figure the fulcrum, effort arm, and resistance arm are lettered.

Identify these parts by *letter*.

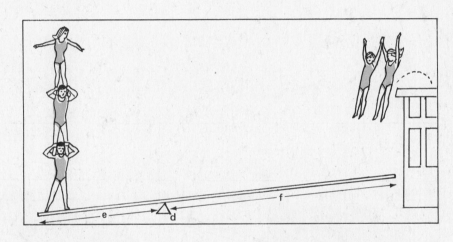

Figure B

1. Fulcrum _____ Effort Arm _____ Resistance Arm _____

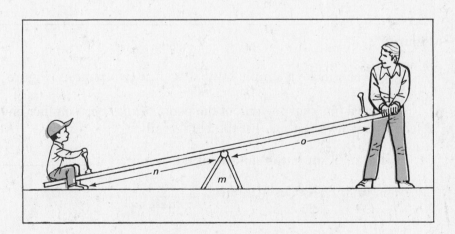

Figure C

2. Fulcrum _____ Effort Arm _____ Resistance Arm _____

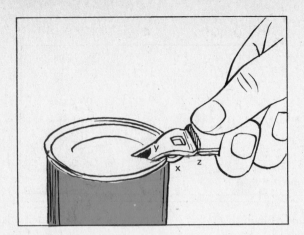

Figure D

Figure E

3. Fulcrum _____

   Effort Arm _____

   Resistance Arm _____

4. Fulcrum _____

   Effort Arm _____

   Resistance Arm _____

MAKE YOUR OWN LEVER

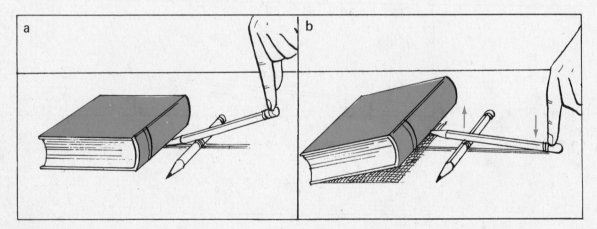

Figure F

You can make a simple lever with just two pencils. Figure F shows how.

Place a book on one end of the pencil. Press on the other end with just one finger. Doesn't your lever let you lift the book easily?

1. Is the fulcrum in the middle of the pencil? _____

2. The fulcrum is closer to the _____ .
   finger, book

Complete each sentence with the terms below. One of these terms may be used three times.

steady	turns	effort distance
lever	multiply	fulcrum
effort	rod or plank	resistance
changes the direction	resistance distance	

1. In this Aim you have begun to learn about another simple machine. It is called the _____.

2. The main parts of a lever are a _____ point and a _____ _____.

3. The steady point that a lever plank rests upon is called the _____.

4. The rod or plank _____ on the fulcrum.

5. A _____ rests on one side of the fulcrum; an _____ presses on the other side.

6. The distance between the fulcrum and the resistance is called the _____.

7. The distance between the fulcrum and the effort is called the _____.

8. When you change the position of a _____, you change the effort distance and the resistance distance.

9. When you change the effort distance and resistance distance, you change the position of the _____.

10. A lever does two jobs. It can _____ a force. It also _____ of a force.

MATCHING   Match the two lists. Write the correct letter on the line next to each number.

1. _____ lever

2. _____ fulcrum and plank

3. _____ effort

4. _____ resistance arm

5. _____ fulcrum

a) parts of a lever

b) distance from fulcrum to resistance

c) steady point for a plank to turn or rest

d) a simple machine

e) overcomes resistance

CONNECTING DOTS

Each player draws a line. If the line completes a box, then the player goes again. Put your initials in the boxes you complete.

```
·   ·   ·   ·   ·   ·   ·   ·   ·   Scoring:
            L   E   V   E   R       empty box counts 1 point
·   ·   ·   ·   ·   ·   ·   ·   ·   box with a letter counts 2 points
        P                           add 10 points for each complete word
·   ·   ·   ·   ·   ·   ·   ·   ·
A       L
·   ·   ·   ·   ·   ·   ·   ·   ·               SCORE
X       A                           Name _____ | Name _____
·   ·   ·   ·   ·   ·   ·   ·   ·                         |
L       N                                                |
·   ·   ·   ·   ·   ·   ·   ·   ·                         |
E       K               R                                |
·   ·   ·   ·   ·   ·   ·   ·   ·                         |
                        O                                |
·   ·   ·   ·   ·   ·   ·   ·   ·                         |
                        D                                |
·   ·   ·   ·   ·   ·   ·   ·   ·                         |
E   F   F   O   R   T                                    |
·   ·   ·   ·   ·   ·   ·   ·   ·                         |
                                                         |
·   ·   ·   ·   ·   ·   ·   ·   ·
    A   R   M
·   ·   ·   ·   ·   ·   ·   ·   ·
```

HOW CAN YOU FIND THE MECHANICAL ADVANTAGE OF A LEVER?

20

M.A. = $\dfrac{16\,\text{meters}}{4\,\text{meters}}$

M.A. = 4

M. A. of a lever: the length of the effort arm divided by the length of the resistance arm

AIM 20 | How can you find the mechanical advantage of a lever?

Try this simple experiment:

Set up your "pencil-lever" again. Place a book on one end.

See what happens when you move the fulcrum.

POSITION 1 Place the fulcrum far away from the book (Figure A). Press down on the effort arm. Notice that it is not easy to lift the book. A strong effort force is needed.

POSITION 2 Move the fulcrum closer to the book—to about the middle of the pencil (Figure B). Press down on the effort arm. Is it easier or more difficult to lift the book?

POSITION 3 Move the fulcrum right up against the book (Figure C). Press down on the effort arm. Compared to position 2, is it easier or more difficult to move the book?

We see that work becomes easier as the effort arm becomes longer. Another way of saying this is, *the longer* the effort arm compared to the resistance arm, the *greater* the mechanical advantage.

You can easily figure the mechanical advantage of a lever. Just *divide the effort arm length by the resistance arm length.*

Here is an example:

If an effort arm is 4 centimeters long and a resistance arm is 2 centimeters long, then the mechanical advantage is 2.

$$\text{M.A.} = \frac{\text{Effort arm}}{\text{Resistance arm}} = \frac{4 \text{ cm}}{2 \text{ cm}} = 2 \qquad \text{M.A.} = 2$$

MOVING THE FULCRUM OF A LEVER

Figure A

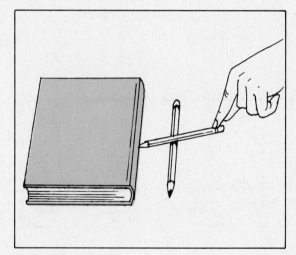

Figure B

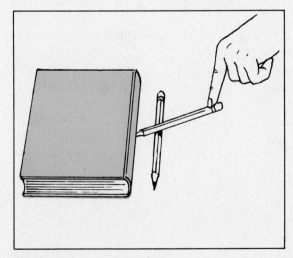

Figure C

1. In Figure A the longer arm is the

   _____.
   effort arm, resistance arm

2. Compared to the resistance arm,

   the effort arm is _____.
   longer, shorter

3. In Figure B, the effort arm has been

   made _____ than in
   longer, shorter
   Figure A.

4. To move the resistance, you now

   need _____ effort.
   more, less

5. The longer effort arm made the job

   _____.
   easier, more difficult

6. In Figure C, the effort arm has been

   made even _____ than
   longer, shorter
   in Figure B.

7. To move the resistance, you now

   need even _____ force.
   more, less

8. The M.A. is _____.
   increasing, decreasing

9. The longer the effort arm, the

   _____ the M.A.
   larger, smaller

10. The shorter the effort arm, the

    _____ the M.A.
    larger, smaller

FINDING THE M.A. Four small levers are shown in Figures D, E, F, and G. Study each one. Then answer the questions. Be careful, one is tricky!

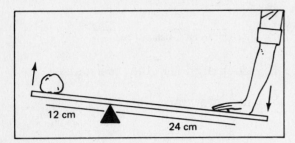

Figure D

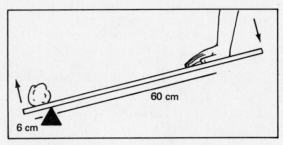

Figure E

1. $\dfrac{\text{Effort arm}}{\text{Resistance arm}}$ = _____ = M.A.

2. A force is multiplied _____ times.

3. A 50 gram force will lift a resistance of _____ grams.

4. $\dfrac{\text{Effort arm}}{\text{Resistance arm}}$ = _____ = M.A.

5. A force is multiplied _____ times.

6. A 10 gram force will lift _____ grams.

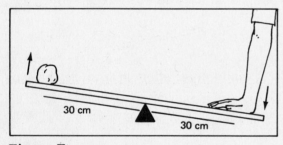

Figure F

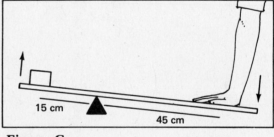

Figure G

7. $\dfrac{\text{Effort arm}}{\text{Resistance arm}}$ = _____ = M.A.

8. A force is multiplied _____ times.

9. To lift a 2 kilogram resistance, you need a force of _____ kilograms.

10. $\dfrac{\text{Effort arm}}{\text{Resistance arm}}$ = _____ = M.A.

11. A force is multiplied _____ times.

12. To lift a 30 kilogram resistance, you need a force of _____ kilograms.

13. Which of these levers makes work easiest? _____

    Why? _____

14. Which of these levers does *not* make work easier? _____

128

MATCHING

Match the two lists. Write the correct letter on the line next to each number.

1. _____ lever

2. _____ plank and fulcrum

3. _____ $\dfrac{\text{Effort arm}}{\text{Resistance arm}}$

4. _____ long effort arm

5. _____ short effort arm

a) = M.A. of a lever

b) large M.A.

c) parts of a lever

d) small M.A.

e) a simple machine

MEASURING LEVER ARMS

Four levers are shown in Figures H, I, J, and K.

Use your metric ruler and arithmetic to figure the M.A. of each one.

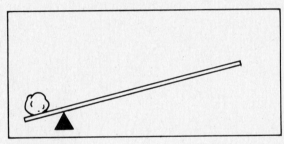

Figure H

Effort arm = _____ cm

Resistance arm = _____ cm

M.A. = _____

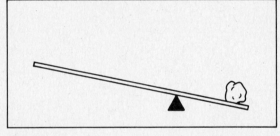

Figure I

Effort arm = _____ cm

Resistance arm = _____ cm

M.A. = _____

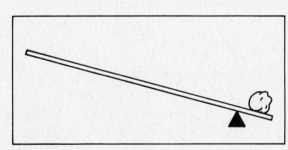

Figure J

Effort arm = _____ cm

Resistance arm = _____ cm

M.A. = _____

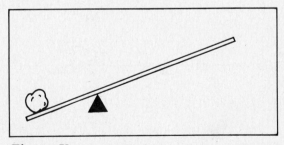

Figure K

Effort arm = _____ cm

Resistance arm = _____ cm

M.A. = _____

Write T on the line next to the number if the sentence is true.
Write F if the sentence is false.

1. _____ A lever is a complicated machine.

2. _____ A lever moves straight with the ground.

3. _____ A lever rotates on its effort arm.

4. _____ Every lever has a fulcrum.

5. _____ The fulcrum of every lever is at the same spot.

6. _____ You can change the M.A. of a lever by changing its fulcrum.

7. _____ You can change the M.A. of a lever by changing its effort distance.

8. _____ You can change the M.A. of a lever by changing its resistance distance.

9. _____ A long effort arm always means a large M.A. (Think carefully about this one).

10. _____ The longer the effort arm compared to the resistance arm, the greater the M.A.

REACHING OUT

Why must long levers be made thicker than short levers?

_____

_____

_____

_____

_____

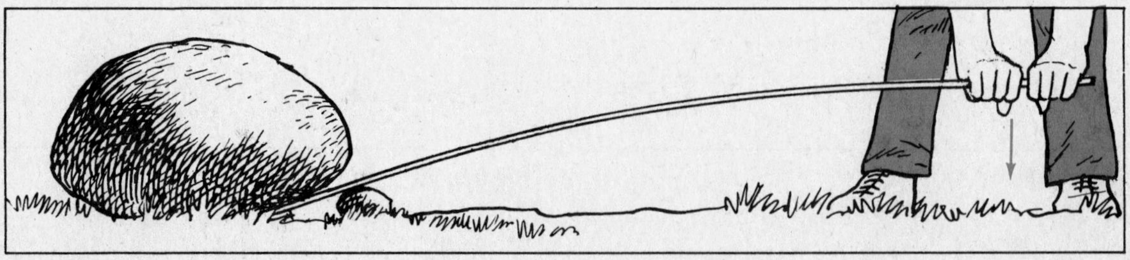

Figure L

WHEN DOES A LEVER BALANCE?

21

rotate: to turn

A seesaw is a lever you can have fun with. You can "ride the bumps"—or you can try to keep it balanced.

A seesaw balances easily—if the people on the ends weigh the same. If, however, one person is heavier than the other, the board *rotates* on its fulcrum. The heavier side rotates *downward;* the lighter side rotates *upward.*

A seesaw can balance even if one person is heavier than the other. The heavier person just moves up a bit— *closer to the fulcrum.* This changes the distance of the lever arm on that side.

If you change the effort distance or resistance distance of a lever, you change the mechanical advantage. This changes the balance. It can make a lever *balance*—or it can tilt (un- balance) it.

A lever is balanced if the turning force on one side of the fulcrum equals the turning force on the other side of the fulcrum.

To figure a turning force, just multiply a force by its distance to the fulcrum.

The formula to test balance is:

EFFORT × EFFORT DISTANCE = RESISTANCE × RESISTANCE DISTANCE

If the value on one side of the equal sign is the same as the value on the other side of the equal sign, then the lever *is* balanced.

If the values are *not* the same, then the lever is *not* balanced. It rotates towards the heavier side. Rotation to the right ↻, is called *clockwise* rotation. Rotation to the left ↺, is called counter-clockwise rotation.

In a balanced lever, the clockwise force equals the counter-clockwise force.

BALANCED AND UNBALANCED FORCES

Study each lever in Figures A, B, C, and D. Then complete the sentences by filling in the blanks.

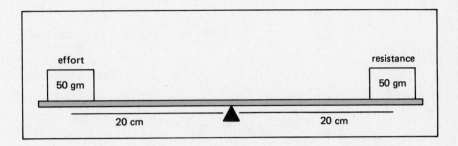

Figure A

EFFORT × EFFORT DISTANCE = RESISTANCE × RESISTANCE DISTANCE

Effort = 50 grams
Effort distance = 20 centimeters

Resistance = 50 grams
Resistance distance = 20 centimeters

50 × 20 = 1000 gram-centimeters

50 × 20 = 1000 gram-centimeters

1. The effort side _____ equal the resistance side.
   does, does not

2. The lever in Figure A _____ balanced.
   is, is not

3. The lever in Figure A _____ rotate by itself.
   will, will not

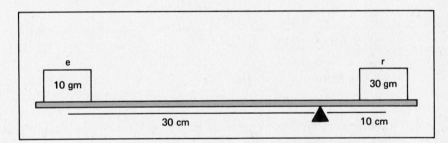

Figure B

EFFORT × EFFORT DISTANCE = RESISTANCE × RESISTANCE DISTANCE

Effort = 10 grams
Effort distance = 30 centimeters

Resistance = 30 grams
Resistance distance = 10 centimeters

10 × 30 = 300 gram-centimeters

30 × 10 = 300 gram-centimeters

4. In Figure B the effort side _____ equal the resistance side.
   does, does not

5. The lever in Figure B _____ balanced.
   is, is not

6. This lever _____ rotate by itself.
   will, will not

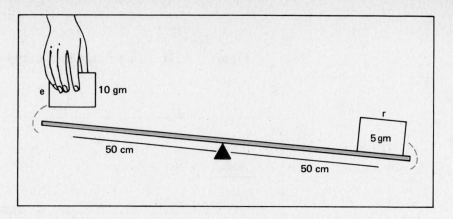

Figure C

EFFORT × EFFORT DISTANCE = RESISTANCE × RESISTANCE DISTANCE

Effort = 10 grams
Effort distance = 50 centimeters

Resistance = 5 grams
Resistance distance = 50 centimeters

$$10 \times 50 = 500$$

$$5 \times 50 = 250$$

Effort side = 500 gram-centimeters

Resistance side = 250 gram-centimeters

7. When the effort weight is added in Figure C, the resistance _____ equal the effort.
<small>will, will not</small>

8. The resistance side is _____ than the effort side.
<small>stronger, weaker</small>

9. The lever in Figure C _____ balance.
<small>will, will not</small>

10. This lever _____ turn by itself.
<small>will, will not</small>

11. With the effort weight, this lever will turn _____.
<small>clockwise, counter-clockwise</small>

12. Draw arrows on dotted lines of Figure C to show how the lever will rotate when the effort weight is added.

13. The force on the left side _____ equal the force on the right side.
<small>will, will not</small>

14. The force will be greater on the _____ side.
<small>right, left</small>

15. The force will be less on the _____ side.
<small>right, left</small>

16. The lever in Figure C _____ balance.
<small>will, will not</small>

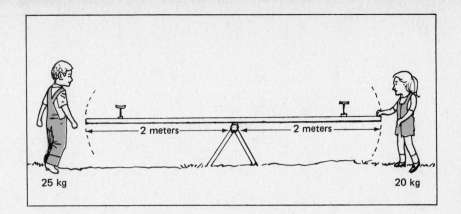

Figure D

The two children in Figure D are going to sit on the ends of this seesaw.

17. This lever _____ rotate.
    will, will not

18. This lever will rotate _____.
    clockwise, counter-clockwise

19. Draw arrows on the dotted lines of Figure D to show how the lever will rotate when the children sit down.

Two levers are shown in Figures E and F. Study each one. Then answer the questions under each figure.

The position shown may *not* help you.

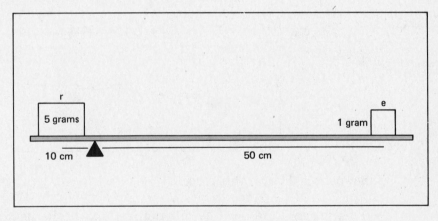

Figure E

1. Effort = _____   Effort Distance = _____

   EFFORT × EFFORT DISTANCE = _____

   Resistance = _____   Resistance Distance = _____

   RESISTANCE × RESISTANCE DISTANCE = _____

   Will this lever balance? _____

   Will it turn by itself? _____

135

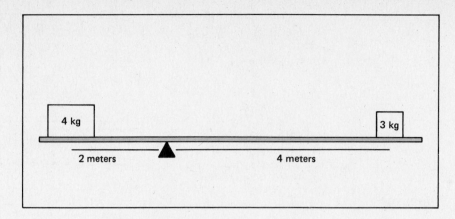

Figure F

2. Effort = _____ Effort Distance = _____

    EFFORT × EFFORT DISTANCE = _____

    Resistance = _____ Resistance Distance = _____

    RESISTANCE × RESISTANCE DISTANCE = _____

    Will this lever turn by itself? _____

    In which direction? _____

REACHING OUT

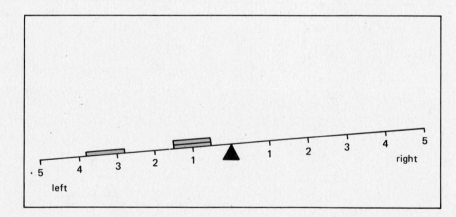

Figure G

Three pennies are on this lever.

You can balance the lever by moving *just one* of the pennies.

How do you do it? _____

_____

_____

_____

136

HOW DO OBJECTS BALANCE?

22

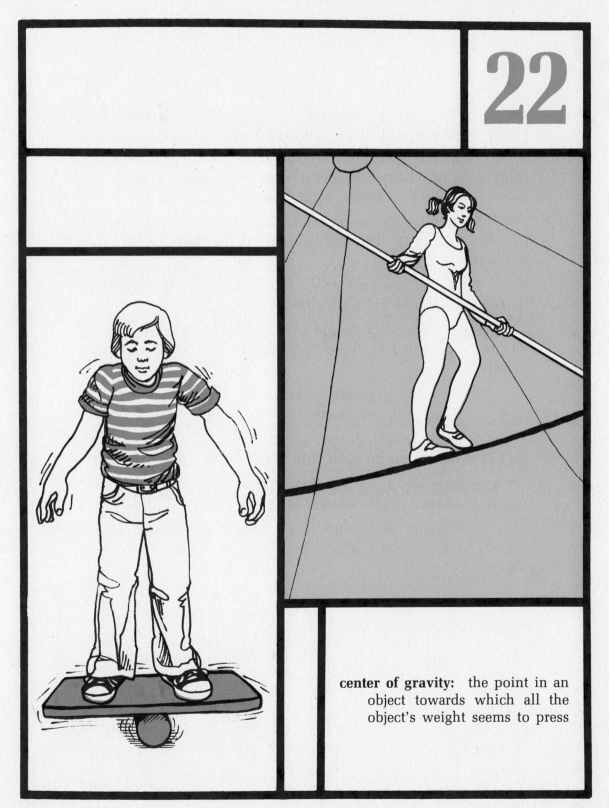

center of gravity: the point in an object towards which all the object's weight seems to press

AIM 22 | How do objects balance?

Try a simple experiment. It will teach you a great deal about balance. Chances are you have tried it before.

Pick up a meter stick. Try to balance it on your fingertip (Figure A). At what point does it balance? A meter stick should balance at 50 centimeters—right in the center.

Now move the meter stick slightly to the right. It will tip over (Figure B). The same thing will happen if you move it slightly to the left.

Why does a ruler balance in the middle? Do all objects balance in the middle? Let us find the answer.

Every object has weight. *All* this weight seems to press towards a point *inside* the object. We call this point its *center of gravity*.

The center of gravity divides the weight of an object *evenly*. An object *balances* and *rotates* on its center of gravity.

A meter stick balances at 50 cm. This is *its* center of gravity. The weight on each side of the 50 cm point is *equal*.

A ruler has a *regular* shape. The center of gravity of a regularly shaped object usually is in the middle of the object.

The center of gravity of an irregularly shaped object usually is *not* in the middle. It is found closer to the heavier side.

Study Figures A, B, and C. Then answer the questions.

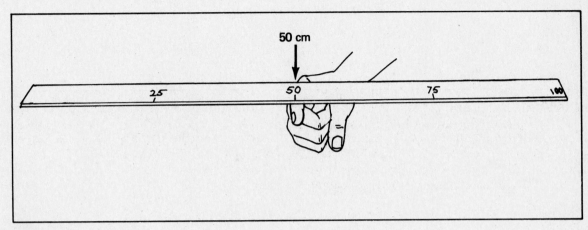

Figure A

1. The ruler in Figure A is _____ centimeters long.

2. The ruler _____ balanced.
   _{is, is not}

3. The center of gravity is at _____ cm.

4. The center of gravity _____ at the middle.
   _{is, is not}

5. A ruler has _____ shape.
   _{a regular, an irregular}

6. The center of gravity of a regularly shaped object is _____ in the middle.
   _{usually, always}

7. If this ruler weighs 150 grams, then,

   a) the weight from 0 cm to 50 cm is _____ grams.

   b) the weight from 50 cm to 100 cm is _____ grams.

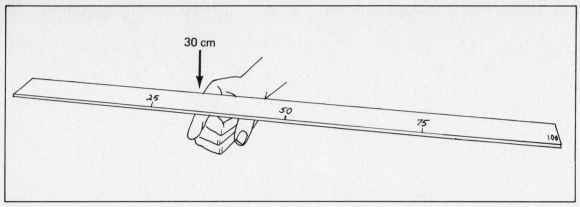

Figure B

8. The finger in Figure B _____ at the middle of the ruler.
   is, is not

9. The ruler _____ balanced.
   is, is not

10. The ruler _____ resting on its center of gravity.
    is, is not

11. There is more weight on the _____ side.
    right, left

12. There is less weight on the _____ side.
    right, left

13. The ruler is rotating towards its _____ side.
    heavier, lighter

14. The spoon in Figure C _____
    is, is not

    turning. It _____ balanced.
    is, is not

15. The spoon _____ resting
    at its middle. is, is not

16. There is more *length* on the

    _____ side.
    handle, bowl

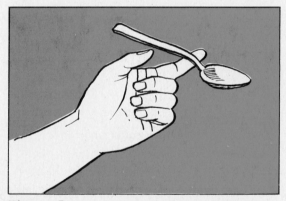

Figure C

17. A spoon has _____ shape.
    a regular, an irregular

18. The center of gravity of an irregularly shaped object usually _____
    at its middle. is, is not

REGULAR OR IRREGULAR?

Twelve objects are shown in Figure D. Some are regular, some are irregular. Study them. Then:

1. Put a check (√) in the *regular* objects.

2. Put an X in the *irregular* objects.

3. Put a dot (●) where you think the center of gravity is in each figure.

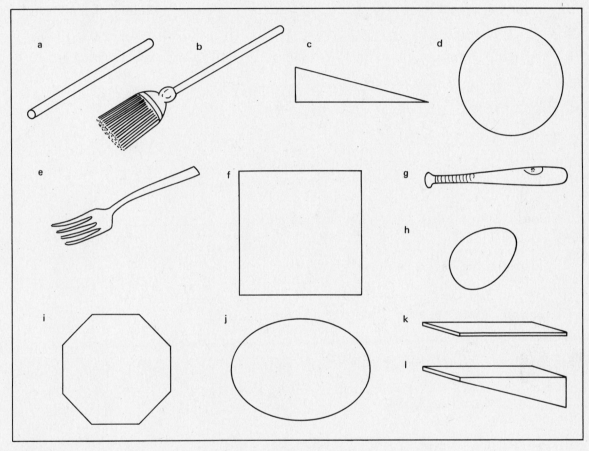

Figure D

Unscramble each of the following to form a word or term that you have read in this Aim.

1. VATYRIG   _____

2. CANLEAB   _____

3. RENTEC   _____

4. GALERRU   _____

5. REALGURRI   _____

USING YOUR HEAD AND YOUR EXPERIENCES

1. An object _____ center of gravity.
   has only one, can have more than one

2. The center of gravity of an object _____ always at its center.
   is, is not

3. Moving an object _____ change its center of gravity. (Think carefully
   does, does not
   before answering!)

4. Adding a weight to an object _____ change its center of gravity.
   does, does not

5. Changing the shape of an object _____ change its center of gravity.
   can, cannot

WHAT DO YOU THINK?

1. Does the earth have a center of gravity? _____
   yes, no

2. Does a piece of dust have a center of gravity? _____
   yes, no

3. Does an atom have a center of gravity? _____
   yes, no

4. Do *you* have a center of gravity? _____
   yes, no

5. Does *every* object have a center of gravity? _____
   yes, no

WHY DO OBJECTS TILT OVER?

23

stable: steady; not likely to tilt

unstable: not steady; likely to tilt

base: the bottom surface of an object; an object rests on its base

AIM 23 | Why do objects tilt over?

The famous Tower of Pisa was started in 1175. Before three stories were built, it began to lean. Since then it has been called the Leaning Tower of Pisa. Scientists are trying to find a way to stop the leaning. If the leaning does not stop, the Tower will tilt too far. Then it will come crashing to the ground.

Why would this tower fall? Why does any object tilt over?

You have learned that every object has its own center of gravity. It is found in different spots in different objects. *It is the location of the center of gravity that keeps an object standing—or—makes it tilt over.*

- If the center of gravity falls *inside* the base, an object will *not* tilt over.

- If the center of gravity falls *outside* the base, an object *will* tilt over.

For example, the center of gravity of this object falls *within* its base. It will *not* tilt over.

The center of gravity of *this* object falls *outside* its base. It *will* tilt over.

Objects that tilt over easily are said to be *unstable*. Objects that do *not* tilt over easily are said to be *stable*. Some objects are more stable than others.

An object is most stable when:

- it has a *wide base,* and
- its center of gravity is *low* and *near the middle of the base.*

You can make an object more stable in two ways:

(1) Make the base wider.

(2) Keep most of the weight near the base. This lowers the center of gravity.

EXAMPLES OF STABLE AND UNSTABLE OBJECTS

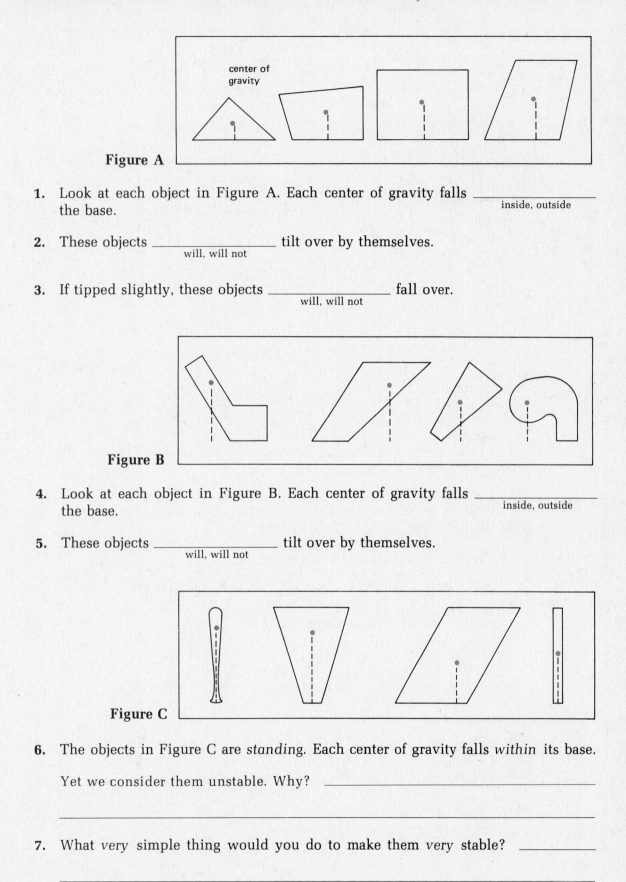

Figure A

1. Look at each object in Figure A. Each center of gravity falls _____ the base.

   inside, outside

2. These objects _____ tilt over by themselves.

   will, will not

3. If tipped slightly, these objects _____ fall over.

   will, will not

Figure B

4. Look at each object in Figure B. Each center of gravity falls _____ the base.

   inside, outside

5. These objects _____ tilt over by themselves.

   will, will not

Figure C

6. The objects in Figure C are *standing*. Each center of gravity falls *within* its base. Yet we consider them unstable. Why? _____

   _____

7. What *very* simple thing would you do to make them *very* stable? _____

   _____

Match the two lists. Write the correct letter on the line next to each number.

1. _____ center of gravity

2. _____ stable objects

3. _____ unstable objects

4. _____ adding weight to the top

5. _____ adding weight to the bottom

a) do not tip over easily

b) lowers center of gravity

c) raises center of gravity

d) where all the weight of an object seems to press

e) tip over easily

TRUE OR FALSE Write T on the line next to the number if the sentence is true. Write F if the sentence is false.

1. _____ Every object has a center of gravity.

2. _____ You can change a center of gravity.

3. _____ Changing a shape can change the center of gravity.

4. _____ Stable objects tip over easily.

5. _____ The center of gravity of a stable object falls outside its base.

6. _____ A wide base makes an object more stable.

7. _____ Every object has more than one base.

8. _____ You can make any object unstable by tilting it.

9. _____ *Any* amount of tilt will make an object unstable. (Think about this one carefully!)

10. _____ Every object has a stable position.

STABLE OR UNSTABLE?

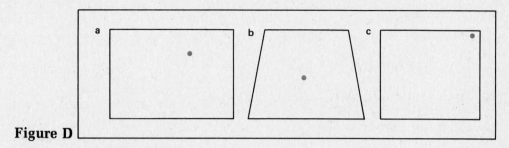

Figure D

1. Look at Figure D. The dots show the center of gravity for each object. All the objects

   in Figure D are _____.
   _{stable, unstable}

2. Which one is *most* stable? _____ Why? _____

3. Which one is *least* stable? _____ Why? _____

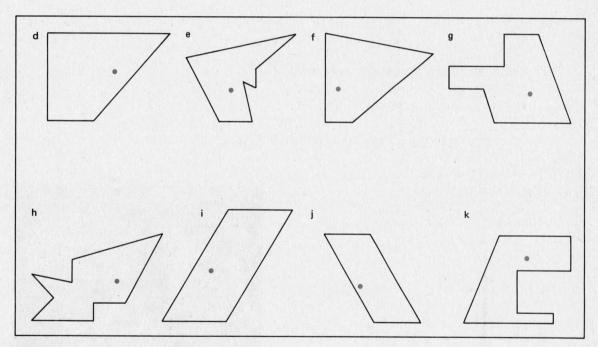

Figure E

    Look at Figure E. Some of the objects are stable. Some are unstable. Place them, by letters, in the correct group.

4. Stable objects _____

   _____

5. Unstable objects _____

   _____

MORE STABLE OR LESS STABLE?

Each of the following makes an object either more stable or less stable. Which one is it? Write your answers on the blank lines.

1. Low center of gravity. _____

2. High center of gravity. _____

3. Center of gravity at edge. _____

4. Center of gravity in middle. _____

5. Add weight at bottom. _____

6. Add weight at top. _____

7. Make the base wider. _____

8. Make the base narrower. _____

REACHING OUT

There is an object you know *very* well.

It has *no* unstable position.

Its center of gravity always falls within its base—no matter how you place the object.

What is this object?

_____

Figure F

148

HOW CAN OBJECTS OF THE SAME SIZE HAVE DIFFERENT WEIGHTS?

volume: the amount of space matter takes up; its length × width × height

density: the weight of a kind of matter per unit of volume

graduate: a container that measures liquid volume

AIM 24 | How can objects of the same size have different weights?

Rocks are heavy. A small box of rocks weighs a lot. Yet a box of the same size containing corks weighs very little.

How can objects that are the same size have different weights? Scientists explain it this way:

All matter is made up of *atoms*. And atoms have weight. Some matter has heavier atoms than others. The heavier the atoms, the greater the weight.

Matter has weight. It also takes up space. The amount of space that matter takes up is called *volume*.

The atoms of some kinds of matter are more tightly packed than the atoms of other kinds. More atoms in a volume mean more weight too.

Two properties of matter are important in the pull of gravity:

(1) the weight of each atom
(2) the *number of atoms* in a given volume

The weight of a given volume of matter is called its *density*.

It is *differences in densities* that give objects of the same size different weights.

For example, gold is about twice as *dense* as copper. This means that if a piece of copper weighs *50* grams, then a piece of gold the *same size* would weigh *100* grams.

How do you figure density? It is easy. Use this simple formula.

$$\text{Density} = \frac{\text{weight}}{\text{volume}}$$

The facing page shows how to figure volume and how to use this formula.

FIGURING VOLUME

Volume is measured in *cubic* units. One common cubic unit is a *cubic centimeter* (cc).

The volume of an object shaped like a box can be found by multiplying three numbers: *length, width,* and *height.*

Example: What is the volume of a box 5 centimeters long, 3 centimeters wide, and 2 centimeters high?

volume = l × w × h
volume = 5 cm × 3 cm × 2 cm
        (5 × 3 × 2 = 30)
volume = 30 *cubic* centimeters

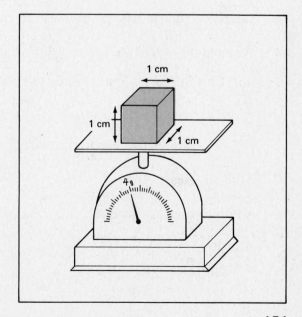

Figure A

This means that 30 one-cubic centimeter boxes can fit inside this box.

Figure B

FIGURING DENSITY

Now let us say that this same 30 cubic centimeter box weighs 120 grams. Let us find its density.

$$\text{Density} = \frac{\text{weight}}{\text{volume}}$$

$$\text{Density} = \frac{120 \text{ grams (g)}}{30 \text{ cubic centimeters (cc)}}$$
           (120 ÷ 30 = 4)

Density = 4 grams per cubic centimeter
           (4 g/cc)

Another way of saying this is:

Each cubic centimeter of this substance weighs 4 grams.

Figure C

COMPARING DENSITIES

Equal volumes of *different* substances have *different* weights.

Each one of these cubes actually shows one cubic centimeter.

Each substance has a different weight.

Each substance has a different *density*.

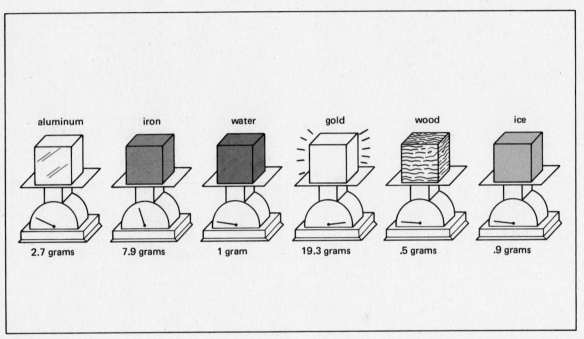

Figure D

Answer these questions.

1. Which substance has the greatest density? _____

2. Which substance has the lowest density? _____

3. Iron, aluminum, and gold are metals. Which of the metals has the greatest density?

   _____

   Which of the metals has the lowest density? _____

   Take a guess:

4. Anything that is *less dense* than water will float. Which two substances will float

   on water? _____ _____

UNDERSTANDING DENSITY

Figure E shows a solid iron cube and a solid aluminum cube. Study the figure. Then fill in the blanks.

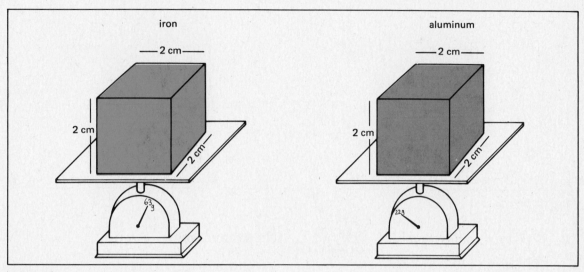

Figure E

1. The volume of the piece of iron is _____ cubic centimeters.

2. The volume of the piece of aluminum is _____ cubic centimeters.

3. The volumes _____ the same.

are, are not

4. They _____ weigh the same.

do, do not

5. The _____ is heavier.

aluminum, iron

6. Iron is _____ dense than aluminum.

more, less

7. Aluminum is _____ dense than iron.

more, less

8. Iron is _____ more dense than aluminum.

sometimes, always

9. Aluminum is _____ less dense than iron.

sometimes, always

10. Iron _____ weighs more than aluminum.

always, sometimes

11. Aluminum _____ weigh more than iron.

can, can never

} These are tricky. *Think* before answering!

UNDERSTANDING VOLUME AND DENSITY

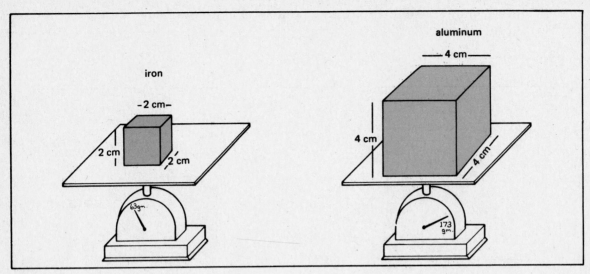

Figure F

1. We know that iron is _____ than aluminum.

   denser, less dense

2. A volume of iron weighs _____ than an equal volume of aluminum.

   more, less

   Now look at Figure F.

3. In Figure F the aluminum weighs _____ than the iron.

   more, less

4. This _____ mean that aluminum is more dense than iron.

   does, does not

5. The aluminum weighs more because there is a _____ volume of

   larger, smaller

   aluminum than there is of iron.

MATCHING   Match the two lists. Write the correct letter on the line next to each number.

1. _____ mass   a) formula for density

2. _____ volume   b) the amount of matter in a substance

3. _____ density   c) formula for volume

4. _____ length × width × height   d) the weight of a given volume

5. _____ $\dfrac{\text{weight (mass)}}{\text{volume}}$ e) the amount of space matter takes up

154

FINDING DENSITIES

For each of the examples below, first, find the volume. Then find the density. The first one has been done for you.

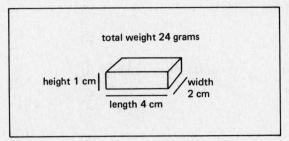

Figure G

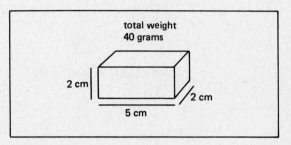

Figure H

1. Finding volume

Volume = l × w × h

Volume = 4 × 2 × 1

Volume = 8 cubic centimeters (cc)

Finding density

Density = $\dfrac{\text{weight}}{\text{volume}}$

Density = $\dfrac{24 \text{ grams}}{8 \text{ cubic centimeters}}$

Density = 3 grams/cubic centimeter

2. Finding volume

Volume = l × w × h

Volume = _____

Volume = _____ cc

Finding density

Density = $\dfrac{\text{weight}}{\text{volume}}$

Density = $\dfrac{\text{_____ g}}{\text{_____ cc}}$

Density = _____ grams/cc

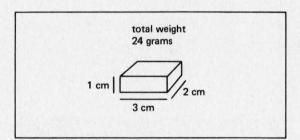

Figure I

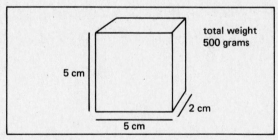

Figure J

3. Volume = l × w × h

Volume = _____

Volume = _____ cc

Density = $\dfrac{\text{weight}}{\text{volume}}$

Density = $\dfrac{\text{_____ g}}{\text{_____ cc}}$

Density = _____ g/cc

4. Volume = l × w × h

Volume = _____

Volume = _____ cc

Density = $\dfrac{\text{weight}}{\text{volume}}$

Density = $\dfrac{\text{_____ g}}{\text{_____ cc}}$

Density = _____ g/cc

Write T on the line next to the number if the sentence is true. Write F if the sentence is false.

1. _____ All matter has weight and takes up space.

2. _____ All atoms weigh the same.

3. _____ An atom of iron weighs more than an atom of aluminum.

4. _____ Feathers can weigh more than rocks.

5. _____ Density has to do only with weight.

6. _____ Volume tells us how much matter weighs.

7. _____ Ice floats on water.

8. _____ Ice is more dense than water.

9. _____ Equal volumes always mean equal weight.

10. _____ A centimeter is a measure of *volume*.

REACHING OUT

A measuring cup or *graduate* measures *liquid volume*.

One measurement of volume is the cubic centimeter. Another is the milliliter. One milliliter (ml) = one cubic centimeter.

1. What volume of liquid is in this graduate? _____

2. How can you use a *graduate, water,* and a piece of *string* to find the *volume* of an odd-shaped object like a rock?

_____

_____

_____

_____

_____

_____

_____

Figure K

WHY DOES A SHIP FLOAT?

25

submerge: to go under water

hull: the bowl-shaped body of a ship

AIM 25 | Why does a ship float?

When you throw a rock into water, it sinks. It sinks because a rock is *denser* than water. When you throw wood into water, it *floats*. It floats because wood is *less dense* than water.

Objects that are denser than water sink in water.

Objects that are less dense than water, float on water.

Here is another comparison.

The density of water is 1 gram per cubic centimeter.

The density of steel is nearly 8 grams per cubic centimeter. This is eight times denser than water.

Steel, then, should sink in water—and it *does*. Yet a steel ship that weighs 100 thousand tons or more *floats* on water.

How can this be explained? *Why* do steel ships float?

The answer is simple. A ship may be made of steel. But only a small part of its *volume* is steel. Because of the shape of the hull, most of the ship's volume is *air*. Air is *less dense* than water.

The density of a ship, then, is not just the density of the metal. It is the density of the metal, the air in the hull, and all the other things in the ship. Altogether, the density is less than the density of water. Objects that are less dense than water float in water. That is why a ship floats.

UNDERSTANDING FLOATING

A flat piece of metal has no air trapped within its border. All its volume is metal. All its density is metal.

Figure A

Figure B

Metal is denser than water. It sinks in water.

What happens when you shape the metal like a bowl—or a ship?

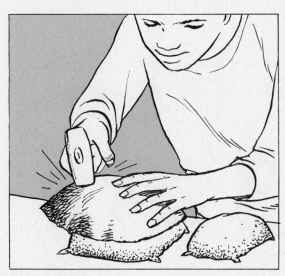

Figure C

Figure D

The new shape has a volume of metal—and *a great deal of air.*

The new shape has a new density. It is the density of the steel as well as the air. And air has a *low* density.

Altogether, the density is less than the density of water. The shaped steel floats on water.

Choose the correct word or term for each statement. Write your choice in the space.

1. Objects that are denser than water _____ in water.
   float, sink

2. Objects that are less dense than water _____ in water.
   sink, float

3. A flat piece of metal _____ have air trapped within its sides.
   does, does not

4. If you place a flat piece of metal on water, it will _____ .
   sink, float

5. A ship is shaped like a _____ .
   table top, bowl

6. A bowl has _____ volume than the flat metal it is made of.
   more, less

7. A ship is shaped like a bowl. Most of the volume of a ship is _____ .
   water, air, metal

8. Air is mostly _____ .
   liquids, gases

9. Gases are _____ dense than metal.
   more, less

10. Making a ship wider and deeper makes it _____ dense.
    more, less

LIGHTER THAN AIR

Figure E

A balloon—not blown up—drops to the ground.

1. What does this tell us about the density of the rubber of the balloon?

_____

Figure F

The same balloon is filled with helium gas. It floats away.

2. What does this tell us about the density of helium?

   _____

Figure G

This is a floating airship. It is called a *dirigible* [DIH rij uh bul].

3. The density of a floating dirigible is _____ than the density of air.
   <small>greater, less</small>

4. What kind of gas do you think a dirigible is filled with? _____

   _____

DENSITY AND SEPARATING SUBSTANCES

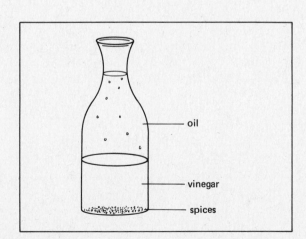

Figure H

Figure H shows salad dressing before it is mixed.

1. The parts separated because they have different _____.
   <small>sizes, densities</small>

2. Which part is *most* dense?

   _____ How do you

   know? _____

3. Which part is the *least* dense?

   _____ How do you

   know? _____

161

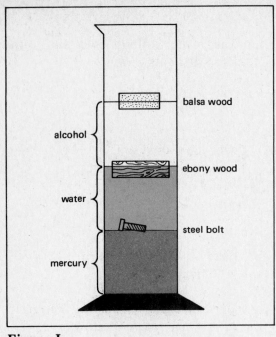

Figure I

Study the mixture in Figure I. Then answer the questions.

4. a) Name the solids in the glass.

_____

b) Name the liquids. _____

_____

5. Which solid is the *most* dense?

_____

6. Which solid is the *least* dense?

_____

7. Which liquid is the *most* dense?

_____

8. Which liquid is the *least* dense? _____

9. Which of these substances have densities *greater* than 1 g/cc? _____

10. Which have densities *less* than 1 g/cc? _____ _____

11. Of *all* the parts you have listed,

a) which is the *most* dense? _____

b) which is the *least* dense? _____

Now let's be a little tricky!

12. There is something in the glass that is not listed. But it is *less* dense than any of

the others. What is this substance? _____

13. What would happen if you were to cap the top and turn the glass over? _____

_____

_____

_____

_____

_____

AN UNDERWATER STORY

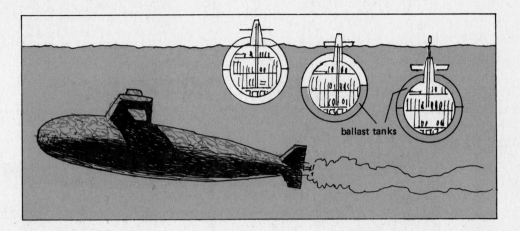

Figure J

A submarine has special *ballast* tanks. Ballast tanks can hold water. When water is let into the tanks, the submarine goes under water. It *submerges*. When the water is forced out of the tanks, the sub rises. It *surfaces*.

1. Adding ballast water makes a submarine _____ dense.
   <small>more, less</small>

2. Forcing ballast water out makes a submarine _____ dense.
   <small>more, less</small>

3. When a submarine is *submerging* its density is _____ than 1 gram/ cubic centimeter.
   <small>greater, less</small>

4. When a submarine is *surfacing* its density is _____ than 1 gram/ cubic centimeter.
   <small>greater, less</small>

REACHING OUT

Gases separate by density. So do liquids. Even a solid, when it is in a gas or a liquid, will find its level by density.

Yet, solids of different densities do *not* separate by density.

For example, aluminum is less dense than iron. Wood is even less dense than iron *or* aluminum.

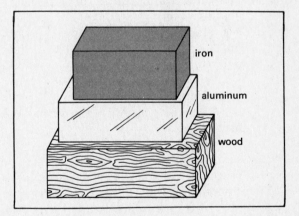

Figure K

Yet, when these substances are placed one on top of another, they do *not* separate by densities.

Why? _____

_____

_____

_____

KEEPING UP WITH SCIENCE

BLIMPS ON THE RISE

An *airship* is an aircraft that is lighter than air. Airships have been called by other names: *dirigible*, *zeppelin*, and just plain *blimp*. Because of their shape, they have also been called *flying cigars*.

Early airships were filled with hydrogen gas—the lightest known substance. But hydrogen can explode and burn. For this reason, whenever possible, hydrogen was replaced by helium. Helium is the second lightest substance. It cannot explode or burn.

An airship rises by itself because it is lighter than air. Motor-driven propellers move it forward. And it can be steered in any direction.

The first successful airship was steam powered. It was flown in 1852 by Henri Giffard of France. By the early 1900s Germany was the leader in airship construction. By 1910 German blimps carried passengers and mail between several German cities.

During World War I, the Germans used airships for observation and for carrying supplies. They also made more than 50 bombing raids over England. The British had military airships, too, but they were not effective.

Several years after that war, the Germans built two giant airships, the *Graf Zeppelin* and the *Hindenburg*. They carried passengers in luxury cabins and dining rooms to many parts of the world.

The *Graf Zeppelin*, named after its inventor Count von Zeppelin, was 800 feet long and 100 feet in diameter. Its living compartments carried 50 passengers and a crew of 20. It could fly as fast as 70 miles per hour. It flew round-trip between Lakehurst, New Jersey, and Germany in 21 days. In the 1930s it was on a regular run between Germany and South America.

In 1937 the *Hindenburg* exploded and burned as it was mooring at Lakehurst. This tragedy ended regular airship service.

During World War II, U.S. Navy blimps protected surface ships from submarine attack. Today, only a few small advertising and news blimps like the Goodyear blimp are in use.

Blimps have great *buoyancy*. They can lift enormous weights. Plans are underway to use blimps as *airborn cranes*. They will lift and transport into place huge loads such as downed giant trees and high-rise building sections. They could help raise sunken ships. And they can do jobs helicopters cannot do.

Transatlantic passenger blimp service is also a possibility. Within a few years, you may look up and see these flying cigars passing overhead. You may even fly to Europe in one.

WHAT IS PRESSURE?

area: the length of an object multiplied by its width

pressure: the force on a given area

manometer: an instrument that measures water pressure

What is pressure?

The date was April 10, 1963. The American submarine *Thresher* was making test runs off the coast of Boston. There were 129 sailors aboard.

Radio contact gave no hint of trouble. Suddenly, there was silence. The *Thresher* was not heard from again.

Planes and ships searched the area. But no trace of the sub was found.

Finally, an underwater camera discovered the terrible truth. Pictures showed pieces of the *Thresher* spread on the ocean floor. The submarine had gone too deep. The water pressure had crushed its hull. Everyone aboard had died.

What is pressure?

PRESSURE IS A FORCE ON A DEFINITE AREA.

Pressure depends on two things:

(1) The amount of *force* on an object.

(2) The size of the *area* the force pushes or pulls on.

Pressure is measured in units of force on a given area. For example, a force of 10 grams pushing on one square centimeter has a *pressure* of 10 grams per square centimeter. We can also write 10 g/sq cm.

Pressure can be caused by the *weight of matter*. The more matter there is pressing on an object, the greater the pressure. Usually, the *denser* the matter is the greater the pressure.

Take water, for example. Water is denser than air. Therefore, water pressure is greater than air pressure. The deeper we go in water, the more water there is above us. The weight becomes greater and greater. So does the pressure.

Natural pressure is caused by gravity pulling upon matter. Solids press only *downward*. Liquids and gases are different. Liquids and gases press in *all* directions. At a given point in a liquid or a gas, the pressure is the same in *every* direction.

TRY THIS!

Outstretch your hand, palm up. Pile several books on your hand—*one at a time.* Notice how the pressure changes.

Figure A

1. A book _____ matter.

is, is not

2. A book _____ have

does, does not

weight.

3. Weight _____ cause

does, does not

pressure.

4. You feel the *least* pressure

   with _____ books.

one, many

5. As you add more books, you feel

   _____ pressure.

more, less

6. You feel more pressure because there is _____ weight.

more, less

7. The area of your palm _____ changed.

has, has not

Now, let's change the *area.*

Pile two of the books on your palm. Feel the pressure.

Now, balance the two books on three fingertips only.

Figure B

8. The weight of the books _____ _____ changed.

has, has not

9. The weight of the books is now

   spread over a _____ area.

larger, smaller

10. The pressure on each of your finger-

    tips is _____ than

greater, less

it was on your palm.

167

What conclusions can we make about pressure?

11. If we keep the weight (force) the *same* and spread it over a *smaller* area we

_____ the pressure.
    increase, decrease

12. If we keep the weight (force) the *same* and spread it over a *larger* area we

_____ the pressure.
    increase, decrease

13. If we keep the area the same and *increase* the force we _____ the
    pressure.   increase, decrease

14. If we keep the area the same and *decrease* the force we _____ the
    pressure.   increase, decrease

15. Solids, like the books, cause a(n) _____ pressure.
                                         upward, downward

MEASURING WATER PRESSURE

The instrument in Figure C is called a *manometer* [man OM uh ter].

A manometer measures *water* pressure. The liquid in the "U" tube *rises* as the pressure becomes *greater*.

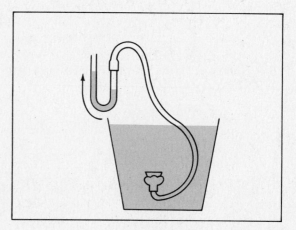

Figure C

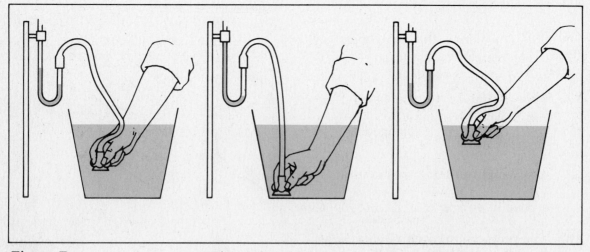

Figure D   **Figure E**   **Figure F**

Figures D, E, and F show a manometer in water. In each one, the manometer "bulb" is at a different *depth*.

Study each figure. Then fill in the blanks.

1. The water level in the "U" tube is   a)   lowest in _____ .

   b)   highest in _____ .

2. Water pressure is   a)   greatest in _____ .

   b)   least in _____ .

3. Pressure is greatest at the _____ of the water.
   <u>top, bottom</u>

4. Pressure is lowest at the _____ of the water.
   <u>top, bottom</u>

5. Water pressure _____ the deeper you go in water.
   <u>increases, decreases</u>

Figures G, H, and I show a manometer in water. In each one, the manometer bulb is in a different *position*.
Study each figure. Then fill in the blanks.

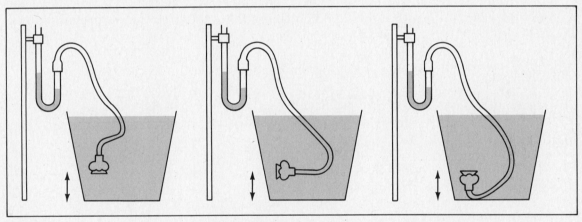

Figure G   **Figure H**   **Figure I**

6. In Figures G, H, and I the bulb of the manometer is at _____ .
   <u>one depth, different depths</u>

7. a)   Changing the position of the bulb _____ changed the water level
   <u>has, has not</u>
   in the tube.

   b)   This means that the pressure _____ changed.
   <u>has, has not</u>

8. This demonstration shows that:

   a)   water presses _____ .
   <u>only downward, only upward, on all sides</u>

   b)   at a given point, water pressure _____ the same in every direction.
   <u>is, is not</u>

ABOUT AIR PRESSURE

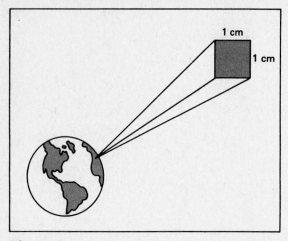

Figure J

The *atmosphere* is the layer of gases that surrounds the earth. It is about 1000 kilometers (600 miles) thick.

Gases do not weigh much. But a layer of gases this thick is quite heavy.

At sea level, air presses down with a force of about 1 kilogram on every square centimeter (14.7 lbs/sq in).

It doesn't sound like much? Well think again! Look at just *one* sheet of this book. The total force on this sheet is about 585 kilograms (1,290 lbs)!

MEASURING AREAS AND FIGURING TOTAL FORCES

Measure the rectangles in Figures K, L, M, and N with your metric ruler. Find the area of each. (Area = length × width) Then figure the total force that is pressing down on each area.

Remember, air pressure is 1 kilogram per square centimeter (1 kg/sq cm).

Example 1 has been worked out for you.

Figure K

1. length = 3 cm
    width = 2 cm
    area (l × w) = 6 sq cm

    Total force = area × pressure

    Force = 6 sq cm × 1 kg/sq cm

    Force = 6 kg

Figure L

2. length = _____ cm

    width = _____ cm

    area = _____ sq cm

    Total force = _____ kg

    What would be the total force if the pressure were 2 kg/sq cm?

    _____

Figure M

Figure N

3. length = _____ cm

   width = _____ cm

   area = _____ sq cm

   Total force = _____ kg

   What would be the total force if the pressure were 3 kg/sq cm?

   _____

4. length = _____ cm

   width = _____ cm

   area = _____ sq cm

   Total force = _____ kg

   What would be the total force if the pressure were 5 kg/sq cm?

   _____

COMPLETING SENTENCES   Complete the sentences with the choices below. One of these may be used twice.

in all directions	downward	pressure
more	higher	deeper
weight	heavier	area
gravity	force	

1. A force on a certain area is called _____.

2. Pressure comes from the _____ of matter.

3. The force that pulls matter downward is called _____.

4. Solids press only _____.

5. Liquids and gases press _____.

6. Pressure increases when there is _____ matter or _____ matter.

7. The deeper you go in water, the _____ water there is above you.

8. Water pressure becomes greater the _____ you go.

9. Gravity becomes weaker the _____ you go in the atmosphere.

10. Pressure is measured in units of _____ over a given _____.

Match the two lists. Write the correct letter on the line next to each number.

1. _____ gravity	a) press in all directions
2. _____ solids	b) a pressure measurement
3. _____ liquids and gases	c) press only downward
4. _____ square centimeter	d) an area measurement
5. _____ 1 gram/square centimeter	e) pulls things downward

REACHING OUT

Where is air pressure greater, high in the atmosphere or on the ground?

_____

Why? _____

_____

_____

_____

_____

Figure O

WHAT HAPPENS TO THE WEIGHT OF AN OBJECT WHEN IT IS UNDER WATER?

27

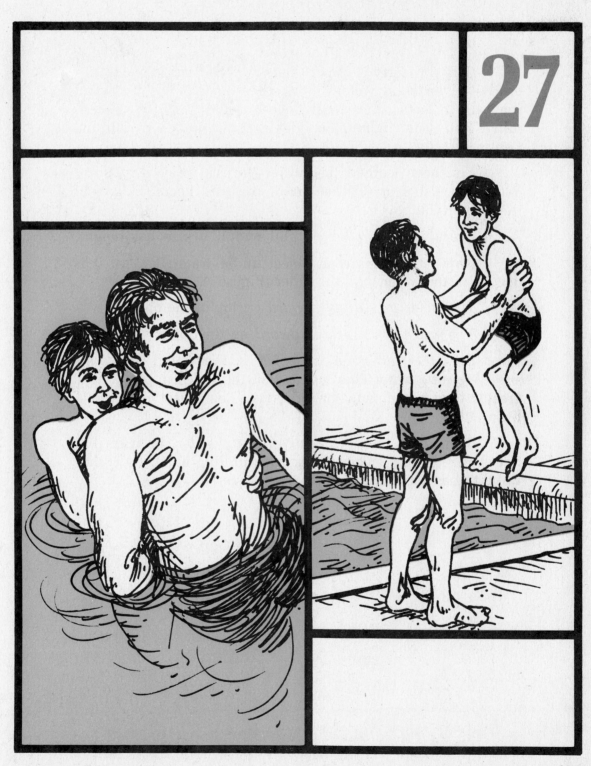

Can you carry a grown man in your arms? You can—easily—*if* he is in water. Things seem much lighter when they are in water. You must have noticed this while swimming. *You* seem lighter. So does anything you are holding. Let us see why.

You have learned that water presses in all directions. You have also learned that water pressure becomes greater the deeper you go.

Every object has length and width. It also has *height*.

Now let's imagine an object under water. Part of it is *deeper* in the water than the other (Figure A).

The water presses *downward* on top of the object.

The water also presses *upward* on the object.

But, the underside is *deeper* in the water. The pressure is *greater* here. This means that the *upward* pressure is greater than the *downward* pressure. The object is given a little "lift."

Remember, the object only *seems* lighter. Its mass has not changed. Neither has the gravity pulling on it. Its *actual* weight does not change.

FILL IN THE BLANKS Figure A shows an object under water. Study the picture. Then fill in the blanks.

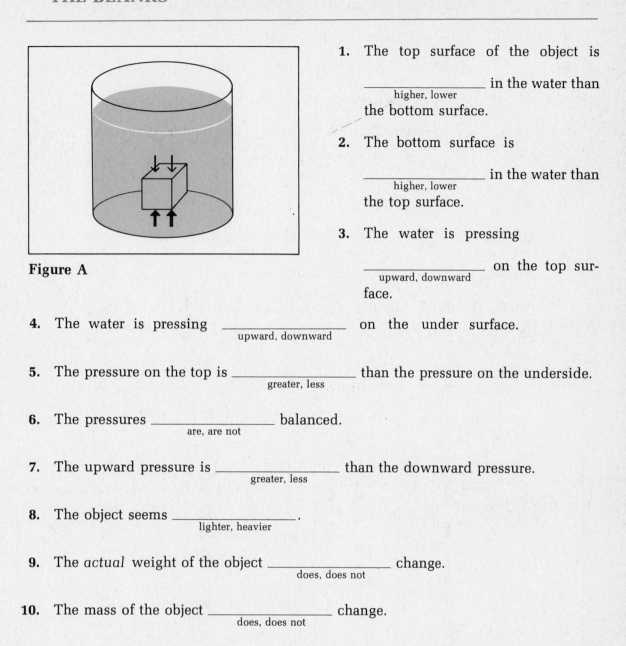

Figure A

1. The top surface of the object is _____ in the water than the bottom surface.
   higher, lower

2. The bottom surface is _____ in the water than the top surface.
   higher, lower

3. The water is pressing _____ on the top surface.
   upward, downward

4. The water is pressing _____ on the under surface.
   upward, downward

5. The pressure on the top is _____ than the pressure on the underside.
   greater, less

6. The pressures _____ balanced.
   are, are not

7. The upward pressure is _____ than the downward pressure.
   greater, less

8. The object seems _____.
   lighter, heavier

9. The *actual* weight of the object _____ change.
   does, does not

10. The mass of the object _____ change.
    does, does not

TRUE OR FALSE Write T on the line next to the number if the sentence is true. Write F if the sentence is false.

1. _____ Every object has length, width, and height.

2. _____ Only water has weight.

3. _____ Weight causes pressure.

4. _____ Water presses only downward.

5. _____ At a given point, water pressure is the same in every direction.

6. _____ The deeper you go in water, the greater the pressure becomes.

7. _____ An object seems to gain weight in water.

8. _____ An object seems to lose weight in water because it has width.

9. _____ At 10 meters deep, water presses less than at 8 meters.

10. _____ At 20 meters deep, water presses more than at 19 meters.

FIGURE IT OUT YOURSELF!

An object that is under water *seems to lose weight.*

When an object sinks, it *pushes aside some water.*

The weight of the water that it pushes aside *is the same as the weight the object seems to lose.*

For example

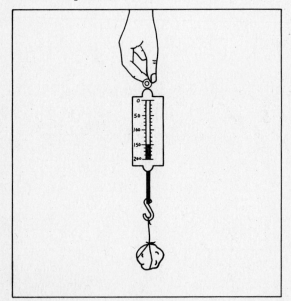

Figure B

In air, this rock weighs *150 grams.*

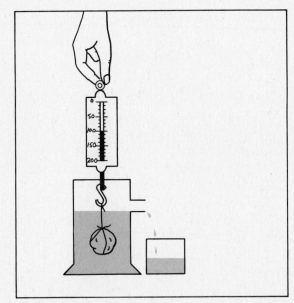

Figure C

In water, it weighs 100 grams.

It seems to have lost 50 grams. . . . .

The rock pushed aside 50 cc of water. 1 cc of water weighs 1 gram. The weight of this water is *50 grams.* . . .

176

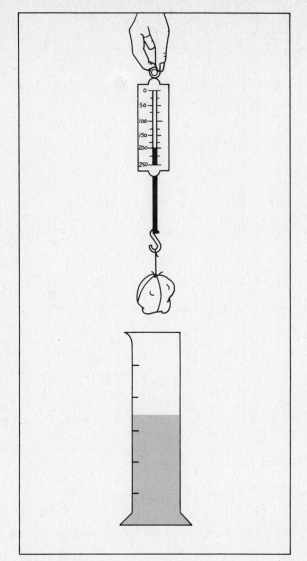

Figure D

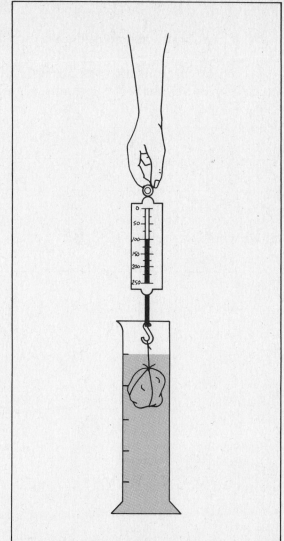

Figure E

Now, try to work out this problem.

1. How much does the rock in Figure D weigh in air? _____

2. How much does it weigh in water? (Figure E) _____

3. How much weight does it *seem* to lose in water? _____

4. **a)** Complete this sentence:

   The weight of water that an object under water pushes aside is equal to

   _____ .

   b) What is the weight of the water this rock has pushed aside? _____

5. How do you know that some water has been pushed aside? _____

REACHING OUT

There is an anchor resting on the ocean floor. It weighs 500 kilograms.

A ship captain wants to raise the anchor onto the ship. The ship has a rope that can lift no more than 490 kilograms. Should the captain use this rope? _____

Why? _____

_____

_____

(Remember what happens to the weight of an object that is under water. But keep in mind where the rope is going!)

Figure F

WHAT HAPPENS TO THE WEIGHT OF A FLOATING OBJECT?

28

displace: to move or push aside

AIM 28 | What happens to the weight of a floating object?

When can a half a million metric tons here on earth weigh *nothing*? It can't—but it can *seem* that way! Many oil tankers are that heavy. But their shapes let them float on water. A floating object seems to weigh nothing at all.

This is what floating is all about. An object floats on water if the *upward force* of the water is the same as the *downward force* of the object. The forces are balanced. And balanced forces equal *zero*.

A ship "finds" this point of balance by sinking part way into the water. Let us trace what happens.

You have learned that:

(a) Water presses in all directions.

(b) Water pressure becomes greater the deeper you go.

The deeper a floating object lowers itself into the water, the greater the upward force of the water becomes. A floating object sinks until it reaches an upward force equal to its own downward force. This is why a heavy floating object sinks deeper into the water than a light object of the same shape. It has to go deeper to reach a stronger upward force. Have you ever seen a cargo ship? How can you tell if it is loaded?

A floating object pushes aside (displaces) a definite amount of water. The amount of water a floating object displaces is equal to its own *weight*. The heavier an object is, the more water it displaces. For example, a 150 kilogram rowboat displaces 150 kilograms of water; a million metric ton ship displaces a million metric tons of water.

WATER PRESSURE AND A SHIP'S PRESSURE

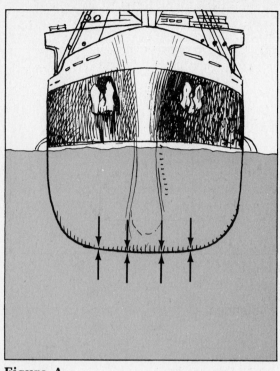

Figure A

1. The arrows in Figure A stand for

   _____.
   _{water, metal, pressure}

2. The downward arrows stand for

   the _____.
   _{ship's pressure, water pressure}

3. The upward arrows stand for the

   _____.
   _{ship's pressure, water pressure}

4. Which of these stands for the greatest upward pressure?

   a)   b)   c)   d)   _____

5. The arrows in Figure A show that the upward and downward pressures

   _____ balanced.
   _{are, are not}

6. This cargo ship weighs 20,000 metric tons.

   a) What is its downward force? _____

   b) How much upward force is pushing against the ship? _____

   c) Where is this force coming from? _____

7. Adding more cargo would make the ship _____ a bit more.
   _{rise, sink}

8. Taking off some cargo would make the ship _____ a bit more.
   _{rise, sink}

9. Adding cargo would make the ship _____ dense.
   _{more, less}

10. Taking off cargo would make the ship _____ dense.
    _{more, less}

181

A FLOATING OBJECT

Study Figures B and C. Then answer the questions.

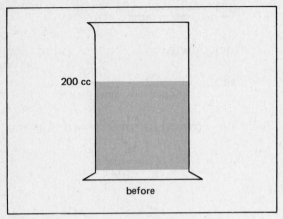

Figure B   **Figure C**

1. The forces in Figure C _____ balanced.
   _{are, are not}

2. The density of the block in the water is _____ the density of water.
   _{greater than, less than}

3. Part of the block is under water. The part that is _____ the water push-
   _{above, in}

ed some water aside.

THREE FLOATING OBJECTS

Figure D shows three solids floating in water. They have the same measurements, but they are made of different materials.

Study the objects. Then answer the questions.

Which of these objects . . .

1. is less dense than water? _____

2. is more dense than water? _____

3. is the most dense? _____

4. is the least dense? _____

5. seems to weigh nothing? _____

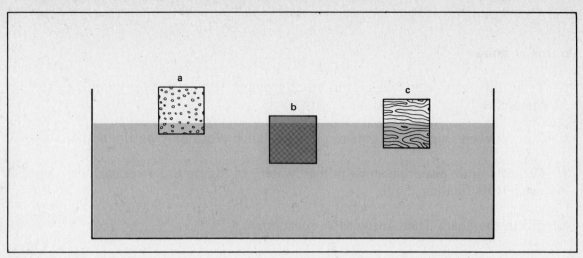

Figure D

6. actually weighs nothing? _____

7. actually weighs the least? _____

8. actually weighs the most? _____

9. displaces the most water? _____

10. displaces the least water? _____

TRUE OR FALSE Write T on the line next to the number if the sentence is true. Write F if the sentence is false.

1. _____ A bar of steel will float on water.

2. _____ The density of steel is greater than 1 g/cc.

3. _____ A steel ship will float on water.

4. _____ A steel ship is mostly metal.

5. _____ The density of a steel ship is greater than the density of water.

6. _____ Part of every floating object is below the water.

7. _____ Water pressure increases the deeper you go.

8. _____ Floating objects seem to weigh nothing.

9. _____ An object sinks when the upward force of the water is the same as the downward force of the object.

10. _____ Every floating object displaces the same amount of water.

PLACING SHIPS IN WATER

Do this at home.

1. Trace the ships found below on tracing paper. (Be *especially* careful in tracing the arrows.)

2. Cut out each ship with a pair of scissors. Cut it close only on the bottom.

3. One at a time, place the ships in the "water" of Figure E. Lower each ship until it reaches its floating depth.

4. Fill in the chart. Then answer the questions.

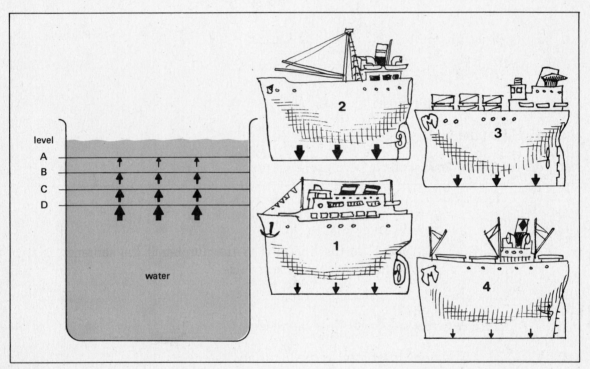

Figure E

Ship	Floating Level
1	
2	
3	
4	

5. Which ship is *most* dense? _____

6. Which ship is *least* dense? _____

7. Which ships have densities *less* than 1 gram/cc? _____

8. Which ships have densities *greater* than 1 gram/cc? _____

184